2.90

PHILOSOPHY IN CANADA/LA PHILOSOPHIE AU CANADA

4

Edited by David Braybrooke with the collaboration of other members of the Department of Philosophy at Dalhousie University.

Ronald M. Yoshida

University of Lethbridge

Reduction in the Physical Sciences

Philosophy in Canada: A Monograph Series

№ **4**

Published for

The Canadian Association for Publishing in Philosophy

by Dalhousie University Press

Halifax, Nova Scotia

First published 1977; produced by Dal Graphics and Typesetting;
printed at the Dalhousie University Printing Centre.

ISSN   0317 - 5480
ISBN   0 - 919936 - 03 - 2

This book has been published with the help of a grant from the
Humanities Research Council of Canada, using funds provided
by the Canada Council.

To Kathryn

CONTENTS

Preface

The replacement view of reduction has struck me as being wrong ever since I first encountered it as an undergraduate, but I have only recently been in a position to lay out what I think is wrong with it. The present work is the result.

I would like to thank Drs. Frank Papp and Shigeru Kounosu for many helpful discussions on technical matters. Neither has read the final draft, so neither is responsible for any technical mistakes. I would also like to acknowledge a study leave granted me by the University of Lethbridge which made the work possible at this time, and for financial assistance in the form of a research grant. Thanks also to Mrs. Lila Spencer who typed the manuscript. Acknowledgement of the support and forbearance of my family goes without saying.

R.M.Y.

Lethbridge, Alberta
August 1975

Introduction

There is a deduction in reduction, or so I shall argue. My argument will consist of two parts: a positive part — the actual arguments for the deductions; and a negative part — the defense against the critics of the deductive view.

I shall accentuate the negative in this monograph, for no one has taken up the cudgels on behalf of the early deductivist view of Ernest Nagel[1] against the anti-deductivist (replacement) view of Paul Feyerabend.[2] Even the main proponents of the deductivist view, Nagel and Hempel, have surrendered under the apparently superior weaponry of Feyerabend and his followers.[3] I shall take up the cudgels, for I do not believe the view has received a fair hearing.

When I say there is a deduction in reduction, I mean that the less comprehensive theory is deducible from the more comprehensive theory **plus** certain auxiliary assumptions, which assumptions include statements describing boundary and initial conditions. (I must and shall have more to say about the auxiliary assumptions later.) This is the thesis presented by Nagel and attacked by Feyerabend.[4] I mention this now because some have thought it worthwhile to discuss the question of whether the less comprehensive is derivable from the more comprehensive theory alone.[5] No one would or should be so foolish as to hold such a view.

The deduction in reduction thesis is usually attacked in two ways. It is attacked directly by taking various particular cases (usually thought to be paradigm cases of reduction) and arguing that the less comprehensive theory is not derivable from the more comprehensive (plus auxiliary assumptions). This is usually done by arguing that the less comprehensive theory is incompatible with the more comprehensive. It is also attacked indirectly by arguing that the main descriptive terms

1 Ernest Nagel, **The Structure of Science** (New York: Harcourt, Brace & World, 1961), pp. 336-97.

2 First stated in P.K. Feyerabend, "Explanation, Reduction, and Empiricism", in **Minnesota Studies in the Philosophy of Science**, ed. Herbert Feigl and Grover Maxwell, Vol. 3 (Minneapolis: University of Minnesota Press, 1962), pp. 28-97.

3 Ernest Nagel, "Issues in the Logic of Reductive Explanations", in **Mind, Science, and History**, ed. Howard S. Kiefer and Milton K. Munitz, Vol. 2, (Albany: State University of New York Press, 1970), p. 121; Carl G. Hempel, "Reduction: Ontological and Linguistic Facets", in **Philosophy, Science, and Method**, ed. S. Morgenbesser, P. Suppes, M. White (New York: St. Martin's Press, 1969), p. 190.

4 Nagel, **Structure**, pp. 352-53 — also see the example, pp. 343-44; Nagel, "Issues", p. 121; Feyerabend, "Explanation, Reduction", p. 46; also P.K. Feyerabend, "How to be a Good Empiricist — A Plea for Tolerance in Matters Epistemological", in **Philosophy of Science; The Delaware Seminar**, ed. Bernard Baumrin (New York: Interscience, 1963) pp. 9, 10.

5 For Example, Nils Roll-Hansen, "On the Reduction of Biology to Physical Science", **Synthese** 20 (1969) 277-89.

of the more comprehensive theory, and the terms definable with their aid, do not mean the same when they occur in the less comprehensive theory. Consequently, though it may look as if the less comprehensive is derivable from the more comprehensive, in fact it is not the less comprehensive theory, but a theory which looks and sounds like it and which is also inconsistent with it.

These claims have been used to infer that (i) the two theories are incommensurable, (ii) replacement not deduction is characteristic of reduction, and (iii) therefore, scientific progress is not cumulative as has been thought.[6]

I shall defend the deductivist thesis first by making some general remarks about the nature of the critical arguments and second by examining the particular reductions that have been discussed in the literature. The general remarks would be empty without a discussion of the particular cases, and the discussion of the particular cases would be repetitious or perhaps chaotic without the general remarks. Thus I shall do both. However, because most of the persuasiveness of the non-deductivist argument comes from the consideration of particular cases, the guts of this monograph is the discussion of the particular cases.

1. The Incompatibility Argument

Almost everyone who has discussed reduction in the sciences has used the following principle: if the less comprehensive theory is logically incompatible with the more comprehensive theory, then the less comprehensive is not derivable from the more comprehensive.[7] C.G. Hempel is a clear case:

> . . . in none of these standard examples does the supposedly reducing theory imply the principles of the supposedly reduced theory; on the contrary, it contradicts them. . . . Thus the notion of deductive reducibility of laws does not fit the logical relationship between such successive theories.[8]

The meaning of the principle is always assumed to be clear, yet a glance at the use of ''logically incompatible'' (and related expressions) shows that it is far from clear. Take, for example,

6 See: Feyerabend, ''Explanation, Reduction'', pp. 28-29; and Thomas Kuhn, **The Structure of Scientific Revolutions**, 2nd ed., enlarged, (Chicago: The University of Chicago Press, 1970), chapter IX.
7 Thomas Nickles, ''Two Concepts of Intertheoretic Reduction'', **The Journal of Philosophy** 70:7 (April 12, 1973) 186, 188; Lawrence Sklar, ''Types of Inter-Theoretic Reduction'', **British Journal for the Philosophy of Science** 18 (1967) 111, 112-13; Hempel, ''Reduction'', 190, 192; Clark Glymour, ''On Some Patterns of Reduction'', **Philosophy of Science** 37 (September, 1970) 340, 351; Nagel, ''Issues'', p. 120; J.J.C. Smart, ''Conflicting Views About Explanation'', in **Boston Studies in the Philosophy of Science**, ed. Robert S. Cohen and Marx W. Wartofsky, Vol. 2 (New York: Humanities, 1965), pp. 159, 160; H. Putnam, ''How Not to Talk About Meaning'', **ibid.**, 207. Also on occasion Feyerabend appears to use this principle: **ibid.**, p. 228; ''Good Empiricist'', pp. 9, 10; ''Explanation, Reduction'', p. 58.
8 Hempel, ''Reduction'', p. 190.

one of the standard theoretical pairs to which the principle is applied, Galileo's law for freely falling bodies ($s = \frac{1}{2}\, gt^2$) on the one hand, and Newton's laws of motion (roughly: "if a body is left to itself $d\vec{v}/dt = 0$, $\vec{F} = d\vec{p}/dt$, $\vec{F}_{12} = -\vec{F}_{21}$") and the law of universal gravitation ($F_{12} = Gm_1m_2/r^2$) on the other. A moment's reflection will show that they are not obviously inconsistent or incompatible in the logician's sense of these words. One's immediate reaction will be to say: "Let m_1 be the mass of the freely falling body and m_2 the mass of the earth, then $m_1g = Gm_1m_2/r^2$ by the second law and the law of universal gravitation, and since r varies as an object falls and m_1 cancels, g must vary, which is incompatible with Galileo's law which says that g is a constant." But what has happened here? It is not the laws alone that are used, but all manner of auxiliary assumptions are used. To name just one, it is assumed that we can ignore the effects of the rotation of the earth. So this tack will not do. Logicians do not assume other substantial (i.e., non-logical) statements to be true to show that a set of statements is incompatible. Yet one can look at other theoretical pairs to which the principle is applied to verify that not assuming so is the rule rather than the exception (in fact I know of no exceptions).

One might argue that "logically incompatible" (and related expressions) are intended as the logician intends them. But while this may be true as a matter of intent, it has the unhappy consequence that those who use the principle apparently always misapply it. Thus to so argue is to do them no favour.

A more plausible and more charitable interpretation to place on all of this is that those who use the principle mean something slightly different than the logicians when they say "**p** is incompatible with **q**". In particular what they mean is that the more comprehensive theory **in conjunction with certain auxiliary assumptions which are true** entails a statement which is logically incompatible (in the logician's sense) with the less comprehensive theory.[9] Since the auxiliary assumptions are true, if the more comprehensive theory is true, the less comprehensive theory must be false. So the less comprehensive theory cannot be derived from the more comprehensive.

This interpretation has a defect similar to that exposed in the first. In the first place, there is little or no reason to believe that one could come up with a set of auxiliary assumptions which are true. For example, we do not know all the bodies in the universe, yet according to the law of universal gravitation they will exert non-vanishing effects on the bodies with which we are concerned (the free-faller and the earth). Second, we do not

9 For example see Feyerabend, "Explanation, Reduction", pp. 46, 47.

know the positions and momenta of even the known bodies with exact precision, and we must know these with such precision if we are to have true auxiliary assumptions. Clearly, the prospects for coming up with true auxiliary assumptions are extremely dim.

In the second place, even if we could come up with true auxiliary assumptions, there is little or no hope of ever solving the resulting equations, even assuming that one could write them down somewhere. The moment we recognize that there are more than two bodies involved, we involve ourselves in the **n** body problem, for which there is no general solution; what solutions there are involve approximations all over the place. Second, the earth is neither a perfect sphere nor a perfect ellipsoid, so we cannot treat it as if its mass were in the center; nor is it clear that it has a center. Further we would have to have the height above (or below) sea level, the distribution of mass on the earth, etc., etc. Even if we had all this information, which we do not, the mathematical difficulties would be insurmountable. Hence no statement which is incompatible with, say, Galileo's law is entailed by the conjunction of Newton's laws plus the true auxiliary assumptions; or at least no one has come within light years of deriving such a statement.

In the third place, there are no good reasons for insisting on the **truth** of the auxiliary assumptions in the analysis of "incompatibility" and there are good scientific reasons for not so insisting. By allowing them to be false we can see the conditions under which the less.comprehensive theory would appear to be true (in terms of the more comprehensive theory), and so we have the basis for an explanation of the success or failure and the limited or unlimited validity of the less comprehensive theory. When we know why the auxiliary assumptions are strictly speaking false, we know why the less comprehensive theory failed when it did and where it is not valid. When we know why the assumptions are approximately true, we know why the less comprehensive theory was as successful as it was and just where it is valid. This is also reason for allowing the auxiliary assumptions to be false on theoretical as well as empirical grounds. That is, it is reason for allowing auxiliary assumptions to be logically incompatible with certain postulates of the more comprehensive theory.

Let me illustrate this with an example: the derivation of the equation of state of an ideal gas from the kinetic theory of gases. For my purposes it will be satisfactory to consider the postulates of the kinetic theory to be the following: (i) monatomic molecules are elastic spheres identical in size and mass for a given substance and differing only in those respects for different substances; (ii) the molecules of all bodies at temperatures above absolute zero are in continual motion with the same mean square velocity at a given temperature, although moving in all possible directions; (iii) Newtonian mechanics applies to the molecular motions; and (iv) the motions are so great that the motion of an individual molecule is entirely free except for the short time intervals during which it encounters other molecules or the walls of the container. [10] In addition to these postulates we need the following auxiliary assumptions: (v) that the molecules of the gas are dimensionless and suffer perfectly elastic collisions, and (vi) that $T = (2/3k)$ ½ $m\bar{v}^2$ where k is Boltzmann's constant and ½ $m\bar{v}^2$ is the mean kinetic energy. (It should be noted, and it never is here or in other derivations, that such assumptions carry with them the tacit assumption that these are the only physically relevant considerations — otherwise the derivation could not proceed.) Now the equation of state for an ideal gas can be derived from the kinetic theory and the auxiliary assumptions. (I realize I am begging the meaning variance question here. I shall make good on this later.)

It should be noticed that the auxiliary assumption which asks us to suppose that the molecules are dimensionless is not only contrary to what we take to be empirical fact, but also is incompatible with the first postulate, which says that the molecules are spherical. This means that if the kinetic theory is true, as we suppose for the purposes of the derivation, the auxiliary assumption is strictly speaking false on both theoretical and empirical grounds. This coupled with the derivation tells us that if the kinetic theory is true, the ideal gas law can have a limited validity at best. The validity of the law is limited by the validity of the auxiliary assumptions, for the law will be true where and to the extent that the auxiliary assumptions are true (according to the kinetic theory). (I am assuming temporarily, and it is usually assumed, that there is no superior alternative to the kinetic theory. Thus the ideal gas equation could not be strictly true when the auxiliary assumptions have but limited validity. This is how the ideal gas law is true to the extent that the auxiliary assumptions are true.) To put it in the usual way, the derivation of the ideal gas equation from the kinetic theory and the (strictly speaking) false auxiliary assumptions shows that the equation is valid when the dimensions of the atoms and the inelasticity of the collisions are negligible. We would not have this knowledge if we did not allow the false auxiliary assumptions to be made. This is the sound scientific reason for allowing the auxiliary

10 Lynde Phelps Wheeler, **Josiah Willard Gibbs: The History of a Great Mind** (New Haven: Yale University Press, 1962), pp. 147-49.

assumptions to be false.

It may be objected that if one allows the auxiliary assumptions to be incompatible with the postulates of the theory, one can derive too much, because from a contradiction anything follows.[11] Whether everything follows from a contradiction is being questioned now by those working with relevance logics. But even if everything does follow from a contradiction, it does not follow that we must or do make use of the inconsistency to derive the equation of state. In fact, the equation of state must be derivable from the postulates of the kinetic theory **minus** the part which is incompatible with the auxiliary assumption. Obviously not just any part of the theory can be held in abeyance in such a fashion, or one could not say the equation was derived from the kinetic theory. I shall deal with this point in section 7. For now suffice it to say that auxiliary assumptions may be incompatible with any non-essential postulate or part of a postulate of the theory in question. By a "non-essential postulate or part of a postulate", I simply mean one which would not change the identity of the theory if it is replaced with a contrary. The assumption that atoms are dimensionless, in conjunction with the other postulates of the theory, does not alter the identity of the theory. It is still the kinetic theory of gases. It is because we do not use the incompatibility that the derivation is informative. We merely hold belief in the postulate, or the part of it which is inconsistent with the auxiliary assumption, in abeyance. And the reason for doing so just is the possibility of a gain in information and understanding.

To return to the main line of argument: there is sound scientific reason for allowing the auxiliary assumptions to be false.

This suggests a still more plausible interpretation of the principle ("If the less comprehensive theory is logically incompatible with the more comprehensive theory, then the less comprehensive is not derivable from the more comprehensive") and the idea of incompatibility in it in particular. It now looks as if the claim of incompatibility comes down to the claim that the more comprehensive theory in conjunction with certain auxiliary assumptions which may be strictly speaking false though approximately true entail a statement which is logically incompatible (in the logician's sense) with the less comprehensive theory. For example, from the kinetic theory plus the assumptions that (i) repulsive forces, which become infinitely great at close range, act between the

---

11 For example, this has been claimed by Tryg Ager, Jerrold L. Aronson, and Robert Weingard in their article, "Are Bridge Laws Really Necessary?", **Noûs** 8 (May, 1974) 119-34.

molecules and (ii) the gas is at such a low pressure that no more than two molecules interact together at any time — (I should add here that it is clear that (ii) is generally false, but on empirical grounds alone) — from these assumptions and the theory one can derive the real gas equation or the van der Waals equation.[12] These auxiliary assumptions account for the dimensions of the molecules and the inelasticity of the collisions. The result is logically incompatible with the ideal gas law. On this ground one might say the kinetic theory is incompatible with the ideal gas law. This interpretation seems to come closest to what those who use the principle have in mind.

But alas when we make the principle jibe in this way with its intended use it turns out to be false, for if two theories are incompatible **in this sense**, one may still be derivable from the other. There is an elementary principle of logic which says: if **p** & **q** imply **r**, **p** may be true though **q** and **r** may be false. Thus by using different **q**'s, so to speak, we may derive different **r**'s. The different **r**'s though both false, may be incompatible, i.e. such that they cannot both be true. So in spite of the fact that **p** and **r** are incompatible in the above sense (because there is a **q**' which in conjunction with **p** entails **r**' which is logically incompatible with **r**) **r** may still be derivable from **p** (& **q**). To continue with the kinetic theoretical example: both the van der Waals equation and the ideal gas equation are strictly speaking false. The ideal gas equation breaks down for dense gases. The van der Waals equation does not work for gases under high pressure. However, both are derivable from the kinetic theory in spite of the fact that they are incompatible in the above discussed sense, one simply uses different, though strictly speaking false, auxiliary assumptions.[13] So the principle which says that one theory is not derivable from another if they are incompatible is, if it is given any appropriate meaning, just false.

I shall call the mistake in reasoning which is based on this principle the **incompatibility fallacy** in what follows.

2. The Meaning Variance Argument

My second general remark has to do with the argument from meaning variance that is employed against the deductivist thesis by Feyerabend and Kuhn.[14] The gist of their argument

---

12 Leonard B. Loeb, **The Kinetic Theory of Gases**, 3rd ed. (New York: Dover, 1961), pp. 151-60; Ludwig Boltzmann, **Lectures on Gas Theory**, trans. Stephen G. Brush (Berkeley: University of California Press, 1964), pp. 341-54.

13 I realize that ''allowing'' false auxiliary assumptions requires a discussion of what assumptions are allowable and what not. I must postpone that discussion until I have discussed the particular cases.

14 Feyerabend uses the argument in most of the things he has written. Kuhn uses it in **Revolutions**, pp. 101-2.

for non-derivability is as follows: the main descriptive terms of the less comprehensive theory change their meaning when they are used within the more comprehensive theory. As a result the sentences of the more comprehensive theory which look and sound like the statements of the less comprehensive theory are not used to make those statements, but are used to make other statements. Thus in most or all of the cases of intertheoretical relations cited in the literature, it is not the less comprehensive theory that is derived from the more comprehensive, but something which looks and sounds like it: "Replacement rather than incorporation or derivation...is seen to be the process that characterizes the transition from a less general theory to a more general one."[15]

The argument is defective on several counts, not the least of which is that an inadequate theory of meaning is used. Since Feyerabend has been the most explicit about this theory of meaning, I shall focus my attention on his discussion.

Feyerabend lays out his theory of meaning in his article "On the 'Meaning' of Scientific Terms" (in **Theories and Observation in Science**, ed. Richard E. Grandy [Englewood Cliffs: Prentice-Hall, 1973], p. 177; references in the text will be to this work): If a term is intertheoretically synonymous, (i) the rules whereby objects are collected into classes must give the same system class or system of classes, and (ii) the changes wrought by the new theory must occur within the classes mentioned in (i). These conditions are effective only if we have made prior "decisions" regarding (a) what notion of "interpretation" to use, and (b) what particular kind of interpretation to use (from amongst those that are consistent with the choice made in (a)). Feyerabend "decides" (without giving reason for that decision) to employ an interpretation which "makes human practice the guide for conceptual considerations and the object of suggestions of conceptual reform" (p. 178).[16] The particular kind of interpretation he has decided on is one in which theoretical principles are fundamental and "local grammar" — that is, "those peculiarities of the usage of our terms which come forth in their application in concrete and possibly, observable situations" (p. 178) — is secondary.

As far as the relation between meaning and theoretical principles goes he gives us two clues; he says: "But in considering (b) we have already decided not to pay attention to any prima facie similarities that might arise at the observational level, but to base our judgement on the principles of the theory

---

15 Feyerabend, "Explanation, Reduction", p. 78, for example.
16 I find much of Feyerabend's theory extremely obscure. However, this obscurity will not hamper the ultimate result.

only'' (p. 179). He also wrote: ''In traditional terminology: [distance in Newtonian physics] and [distance in the general theory of relativity] are **constituted** by the basic principles of [Newtonian physics] and [the general theory], respectively....in earlier papers I have expressed the fact by saying that [they] are **incommensurable notions**'' (p. 180). In ''Reply to Criticism'' (p. 231) he talks of incommensurable **theories** (this is the only place I recall his discussing this particular pair of theories). This is quite a different animal from a notion — the conflation is, however, revealing. And in the ''Problems of Empiricism'' he defined ''incommensurable theories'': ''Two theories will be called incommensurable when the meanings of their main descriptive terms depend on mutually inconsistent principles.''[17] It is clear then that according to Feyerabend the meaning of, say, a descriptive predicate term which occurs in a theory is that thing (entity, property, class, etc.) which satisfies the basic principles of the theory. So, for example, the meaning of ''mass'' (or ''m'') in the special theory of relativity is that property of a body which obeys, amongst other principles, $E = mc^2$.

This will not do. I am quite certain as are others that ''meaning'' is a very vague idea. Putnam is surely right when he says there is a hodge-podge of things that get counted as answers to the question ''what is the meaning of such-and-such a word?''[18] But to say this is not to say that anything goes or that one can ''decide'' as one pleases. It is simply not **that** vague.

Feyerabend's scheme for generating answers has gone beyond the undrawn bounds. As an account of our ordinary or the philosopher's ordinary concept of meaning and incommensurability this view is hideous, for on such an account, the basic principles of our theories would have to be self-referring, necessary, analytic and known **a priori**. It is clear that they are none of these things. It follows that the account is mistaken.[19]

Let me explain by taking a concrete case, say, of ''mass''. On the view being discussed ''mass'' means something like: that inertial property of a body which satisfies the basic equations of special relativity like $E = mc^2$. Then ''m'' would mean: the measure of the inertial property of a body which satisfies the basic equations of special relativity like $E = mc^2$. If true, this would make $E = mc^2$ a self-referring expression. It would say that

(A) The product of the measure of that inertial property of a body which satisfies $E = mc^2$ amongst other things, and

17 P.K. Feyerabend, ''Problems of Empiricism'', in **Beyond the Edge of Certainty**, ed. R. Colodny (Englewood Cliffs: Prentice-Hall, 1965) p. 227.
18 Putnam, ''How Not to Talk About Meaning'', p. 217.

the square of the velocity of light (which velocity satisfies $E = mc^2$, amongst other things) is equal to the energy (which energy satisfies $E = mc^2$ amongst other things).

In short, and to put it crudely, $E = mc^2$ would say "those properties that satisfy me satisfy me". There is nothing wrong with self reference in every case — that is not my point. My point is that the equation does not refer to itself in even an indirect way, and hence "mass" does not mean what it should mean if Feyerabend's view is correct. And that is to say the view is not correct.

Second, if "m" meant this, $E = mc^2$, and indeed all of the "basic" principles of the special theory, would have to be not only true, but necessarily true, i.e. true in all possible worlds. A glance at statement (A) will show why this is so. $E = mc^2$ would have to say in effect "the energy that satisfies me, satisfies me" or, to focus on mass, "the mass which satisfies me, satisfies me". Obviously these are necessarily true. But the equation is not necessarily true, that is, there is a possible world in which $E \neq mc^2$, where $E = kmc^{2.001}$ or $E = mvc$.

Third, all the "basic" principles in which "m" has occurred would have to be analytic, i.e. true in virtue of the meanings of the terms. [19] Again a glance at (A) will show this. But no amount of consideration of the meaning of "E", "m", or "c" alone, prior to the first solid confirmation of the theory, would have shown anyone that $E = mc^2$. And to say at this point that they get their meaning from the theory of Einstein is to beg the question. In fact this objection may be generalized with a new twist: "Confirmation of basic principle" would make no sense, for those principles would be analytic.

Fourth and finally, all the "basic" principles in which "m" occurred would have to be **a priori** true, i.e. ultimately known without appeal to experience, **which they are not**. One need only ask those who did the experiments on binding energy or the creation and annihilation of electron-positron pairs.

It may be said in response that Feyerabend was not giving an account of our ordinary or the philosopher's concept of meaning and that is what the warning quotes in the title of his paper were about. So the above arguments only show that the meaning claim is false. They do not show that the "meaning" claim is false where the purpose of the scare quotes is to warn us that the word is not being used in the ordinary way

19 There is at least a **prima facie** significant difference between necessity, analyticity and **a priori**-ness which warrants my treating these as separate
points. Necessity is a metaphysical idea, analyticity a logico-linguistic idea,
and **a priori**-ness an epistemological idea. I believe more than a **prima facie**
difference has been shown by Saul Kripke, in the now well known article
(talk) "Naming and Necessity" (in **Semantics of Natural Language**, ed. Gilbert Harmon and Donald Davidson [Dordrecht: D. Reidel, 1972], 253-355,
763-69.)

(whatever that is). On this view, the "meaning" of "mass" is determined by contingent statements like $E = mc^2$. This is to say that if things were otherwise, that is, if the denial of $E = mc^2$ were true, the "meaning" of "mass" would be different. One would thereby save the contingency, etc. of the basic principles and still have "meaning" dependent upon the "basic" principles.

But if that is so, a difference in "meaning" is no reason for believing that statements expressed by sentences from different theoretical contexts which contain the term are incommensurable (in the ordinary sense of not having a common standard for evaluating their truth). By hypothesis we have dealt with $E = mc^2$ and **its** denial, and it is a matter of experiment to decide which of the two is true. So the theories are commensurable.

Second, a difference in "meaning" does not exclude derivability. Consider two theories one of which has $E = mc^2$ and $p = mv$ as basic principles, the other of which has $E = mc^2 + mcv$ and $p = mv$ as basic principles. Since meaning and "meaning" are different as has been shown, nothing can stop me from supposing that "p", "m" and "v" **mean** the same in both theories, though they obviously cannot **"mean"** the same in both theories. And since any reasonable concept of a statement would have it that two such sentences (without proper names, definite description or demonstrative expressions) that are used to mean the same thing are used to make the same statement, $p = mv$ is derivable from both theories in spite of the fact that "p = mv" "means" something different in both theories. The lesson to be learned here is that difference in "meaning" does not exclude the possibility of the derivability of the same statement from different theories. The incommensurability thesis and meaning variance argument for non-derivability are the most important and most interesting aspects of Feyerabend's view. So this attempt to save him does so at the cost of wiping out the most interesting and important of his views.

There are other ways of trying to make out a connection between meaning and the laws of a theory which are a bit more sophisticated, but just as defective. For example one might try to get out of Feyerabend's problems by thinking of the meaning as being determined by most of the laws of a theory, in such a way that any one law could be given up. This will not do because it implies that it makes no sense to think of most of the laws of a theory as being false. If one had the apparent negations of most of the laws of a theory, the meaning of the main descriptive terms would be different and consequently the apparent negations would not be the negations of the laws of **that** theory but of some other laws which are expressed via the same vocabulary. But not only does it make sense to think of most of the laws of a theory being mistaken, there are such theories — Kepler's planetary theory and the Ptolemaic theory of the solar system are examples.

One might think in terms of weighting the various laws of a theory according to their importance to the meaning of the term in question. Presumably the most important laws (for meaning) would be those which necessitate the occurrence of a change in meaning if their apparent contrary or contradictories are to be meaningfully asserted. (**Their** contraries or contradictories cannot be meaningfully asserted just because of this feature and they are **apparent** contraries and contradictories because they look and sound like the contraries and contradictories.) Those which are less important are those which give less reason for claiming a change in meaning has occurred when their apparent contraries or contradictories are meaningfully asserted. Finally, those laws which are least important to the meaning involve no occurrence of a change of meaning if their apparent contraries or contradictories are meaningfully asserted.

Such a view is unsatisfactory for two reasons.

First, the laws which are most important for the meaning would have to be self-referring, necessary, analytic and **a priori**, as we have seen, and none of the laws with which the meaning variance theorist is concerned has those properties. So the laws with which he is concerned cannot be most important for the meaning.

Second, the claim that some laws are more (or less) important for meaning change is utterly worthless without a criterion for determining when the meaningful assertion of a set of the apparent contraries or contradictories of such laws is sufficient for a change of meaning to have occurred. But there can be no such criterion. Suppose there were. It would say that the meaningful assertion of the conjunction of the apparent negations of such laws, $(-L_1 \& -L_2 \& ... -L_k)$, entails that the meaning of the main descriptive terms contained in the laws has changed from the meaning they possessed in the theory which contained the un-negated laws L_1, L_2,...L_k. The conjunction of the negations is logically equivalent to the negation of the disjunction of the laws i.e., $-(L_1 \vee L_2 \vee ...L_k)$. If the (apparent) meaningful negation of a statement entails that the meaning of the main descriptive terms has changed, then the un-negated statement is analytic, for example, the meaningful assertion of "Not all bachelors are male" entails that the meaning of the word "bachelor" or "male" has changed, so we know that "All bachelors are male" is analytic. This means that $L_1 \vee L_2 \vee ...L_k$ is analytic. At the same time it is not logically exhaustive, that is, unlike p v -p it does not present all possible states of affairs (-L$_1$ is one possible state of affairs that is not presented). Yet no one of the laws is analytic (this is what the weighting is supposed to avoid). But this is impossible. It is impossible that a non-exhaustive disjunction none of whose disjuncts are analytic should be analytic, because there would be no "source" for the analyticity. If one of the disjuncts were analytic, clearly the disjunction would be analytic in virtue of the meanings of the terms in the disjunct. If the disjunction were logically exhaustive, the disjunction would be analytic in virtue of the meanings of the disjunction and negation signs (p v -p is said to be true in virtue of the meanings of "v" and "-"). But if neither is the case, as is the case here, the disjunction cannot be analytic, for there are no terms the meanings of which make the statement expressed analytic. And this means there cannot be such a criterion for meaning change, and so the talk of weighting the laws is meaningless.

And this is an important point for it also shows that Putnam's idea of a law cluster concept will not work. The idea of a law cluster concept is that the concept (meaning) is constituted by a cluster of laws which determine the identity of the concept (meaning), but in general any one law can be abandoned without destroying the identity of the concept (meaning). Here again the idea is that the meaningful negation of all the apparent members of the cluster entails that a different concept is being used (a difference in meaning). And this implies that the disjunction of the un-negated laws is analytic though it is neither exhaustive nor composed of analytic statements, which we have seen is impossible. So the idea of a law cluster concept will not wash, it is incoherent.

Showing the fundamental faults of the theory of meaning (or "meaning") that has been employed does not show that the basic argument using meaning claims is faulty. I would like to turn to that task now.

There is one principle which has been invoked by both proponents and opponents of the meaning variance view, namely, that common meaning is a necessary condition for derivability. This principle may be put in a more precise form in the following way: if the statement that **p** is derivable from a theory **T**, then the sentence "**p'**", which is formally derivable from **T** and which looks like "**p**" (the sentence which says that **p**), must mean the same as "**p**".[20] Showing a difference in meaning between "**p**" and "**p'**", then, is sufficient to show that the statement that **p** is not derivable from **T**. This principle is of crucial importance to the case for non-derivability. Certainly all

20 The distinction I am making implicitly here between "derivable" and "formally derivable" is that between "consequence" and "derivable" in a logic text like Benson Mates' **Elementary Logic**, 2nd ed., (New York: Oxford University Press, 1972), pp. 63-64, 113.

the meaning variance arguments for non-derivability presuppose the truth of this principle.

I shall argue that this principle is false. It is false because it presupposes a false theory about statements or propositions; and it is false because it is identity of reference, not identity of meaning, that is a necessary condition for derivability.

The principle presupposes that a statement or proposition is the meaning of a sentence. Thus two sentences are used to make the same statement or assert the same proposition when and only when the two sentences mean the same. The crucial part of this equivalence is the implication from left to right: if two sentences are used to make the same statement, they must mean the same. There is considerable agreement that this implication is false. If someone utters of Wilt Chamberlain "He is tall" at the same time that Wilt Chamberlain utters, "I am tall", then they say the same thing and so make the same statement or assert the same proposition. However, no one would say that the sentence "He is tall" means the same as "I am tall", so the implication, and therefore the theory, is false.

In the example it is clear that reference and not meaning is what is important. It is the fact that in the context given "I" and "he" are used by different persons to refer to the same individual that is important. That "I" and "he" mean something different is unimportant in establishing the identity of the statements made. The late E. J. Lemmon gave a criterion of identity for such statements:

> Let S(a) be a sentence containing the uniquely referring expression a, and T(b) be a sentence containing the uniquely referring expression b. For any uniquely referring expression e let rc(e) stand for the reference of e in context c. Then S(a) in c_1 is used to make the same statement as T(b) is used to make in c_2 if, and only if, $rc_1(a) = rc_2(b)$, and for any x, S(x) if, and only if, T(x).[21]

The only part of this that gives me pause is the equivalence condition. I do not think it is strong enough. Suppose the domain is triangles. I do not think we want to say that two persons who utter "a is equiangular" and "a is equilateral" in the same context make the same statement, even though for

21 E. J. Lemmon, "Sentences, Statements and Propositions", in **British Analytical Philosophy**, ed. Bernard Williams and Alan Montefiore (London: Routledge & Kegan Paul, 1966), p. 103. The criterion is generalized for n-ary relations (**ibid.**, p. 104, footnote 17.) Recently, Edgar Page ("Reference and Propositional Identity", **Philosophical Review** 79 [January, 1970] 43-62) has given a counterargument: If "The driver of the van was bald" and "Tom Jones was bald" are used to make the **same** statement where Tom Jones is the driver of the van, then it must not be possible for the first statement to have a different truth value from the second. But if someone else was driving the van, the statements could have a different truth value. Hence they are not used to make the same statement. To the obvious objection that if someone else drove the van, "The driver of the van was bald" is used to make **another** statement, Page argues that the identity of the proposition expressed by a particular utterance of 'The driver of the van was bald' is indifferent to the question 'Who in fact drove the van?'" (Page,

any **x**, **x** is equiangular if, and only if, **x** is equilateral. On the other hand, requiring that the equivalence be analytic which is mentioned by Lemmon[22] is too strong. Two persons who utter "**a** is a bolt of lightning" and "**a** is an electrical discharge from cloud to planetary body or cloud" in the same context make the same statement in spite of the fact that the appropriate equivalence is not analytic.

What is required is that the properties be identical, in Lemmon's terms, that S = T. This implies identity of reference. Now I have no theory of reference, but I do not see that I need one. There seems to be a straightforward sense in which one would say "sulfur", "oil", "snow", and "aspirin" refer to substances of a certain kind; "man", "electron", "gene", and "rifle" refer to entities of a certain kind; "red", "mass", "temperature", and "brother of" refer to qualities or properties; "(the) collision", "(the) charge build-up", and "(the) catastrophe" refer to events; and "to integrate", "to oxidize", "to charge" and "to distribute" refer to actions. So to say that "aspirin" and "acetylsalicylic acid" refer to the same thing is to say that they refer to the same substance, which it turns out is the substance whose formula is $o\text{-}CH_8COOC_6H_4COOH$. It should be noticed that this use of the term cuts across the philosophical sense and reference distinction. According to that distinction the property of redness is not the referent of the word "red", it is the sense of the word, whereas in my use of the term (which I think is more common) the property is the referent.

A criterion of identity for hypotheses, laws, theories and principles may be stated in the following way:

A sentence **p** and a sentence **p'** express the same scientific hypothesis, law, theory, rule or principle if **p** and **p'** are used to claim that the same relations hold between the same referents, regardless of how those referents or indeed the relations themselves are designated, and if the terms which do not refer like "is" and "the" ("syncategorematic" terms) have the same meaning.

Only this criterion will explain how we are able to identify the

"Reference", p. 44). He means "To know what is asserted by a particular utterance of the sentence...does not mean...that we must understand that the reference is to Jones, if it is, and that whether it is to Jones or Smith bears on the identity of the proposition" (Page, "Reference", p. 46). He is of course, right, we do not need to **understand** that the reference is to Jones. But that is not what Lemmon's requirement is about. Lemmon's requirement is that it **be** Jones, if it was, that is referred to **whether we know it or not**, and **whether we understand that the reference is to Jones or not**. In this respect the statement is not indifferent to the question "Who in fact drove the van?" It must be just **that** person who, it turns out, is Jones. If it is **not** just **that** person, then one has a different statement, just as one has a different statement when one uses "The present king of France is bald" once during the reign of Louis XIV and once during the reign of Louis XV.

22 Lemmon, "Sentences", p. 105.

various hypotheses, etc. through the various guises provided by **different** theories, and indeed through the various guises provided by the **same** theory in different formulations. In the former case one need only think of the various ways of expressing the conservation laws in different theories; in the latter case, the second law in various formulations of classical mechanics. For example, in d'Alembert's formulation, how do we know that the equation which I will write ''$f = m\phi$'' is Newton's second law? On the basis of the fact that ''f'' refers to the measure of the motive force, ''m'' refers to the measure of the mass; and ϕ is the accelerative force which is defined by the equation $\phi dt - du$, where dt an du are infinitesimal increments of the time and velocity: in other words ''ϕ'' refers to the acceleration. [23]

Foundations aside, suppose the equation (i.e. the sentence) ''$\vec{F} = md^2\vec{r}/dt^2$'' can be derived from the special theory of relativity with the help of certain assumptions, e.g. that $(v/c)^2$ is negligible. ''F'' refers to a vectorial quantity which is a measure of that which causes a change in motion and which acts in the direction of motion (this latter is not generally true for the relativistic force, except under the assumption that $(v/c)^2$ is negligible), ''m'' refers to the measure of that property of a body in virtue of which it resists a change in motion, and ''$d^2\vec{r}/dt^2$'' refers to the acceleration of the body. Then the equation says that the magnitude and direction of the measure of that which causes a change in motion and which acts in the direction of the acceleration is equal to the product of the magnitude of that property in virtue of which it resists a change in motion and the acceleration of the body. Now the second law of Newtonian physics says just that, i.e. it asserts that just that relation (equality) holds between just those referents.' Hence this equation **is** the second law.

I do not know whether ''m'' in the special theory is synonymous with ''m'' in classical mechanics or not. The only plausible argument for non-synonymy I can think of arises from the fact that ''m'' in the special theory is also called the ''relativistic mass'' as well as just plain ''mass''. One might therefore want to say that ''m'' is synonymous with ''relativistic mass''. One could not say that of ''m'' in classical mechanics without being anachronistic. So a case might be made for a difference in meaning. But that is neither here nor there. The point is that whether this is so does not matter, for in spite of the possible difference in meaning the equation expresses the second law of classical mechanics, as has already been shown.

23 Max Jammer, **Concepts of Force** (New York: Harper & Brothers, 1957), p. 213.

It follows that if "$\vec{F} = md^2\vec{r}/dt^2$" is derivable from the special theory, then the second law of classical mechanics is derivable from the special theory. And the point of deriving this apparently trivial result is that it shows that the only semantic requirement to be placed on derivability is identity of reference not identity of meaning (apart from the syncategorematic terms). The principle which says that common meaning is a necessary condition for derivability is therefore false.

A corollary of this result is that reasoning in accordance with this principle is invalid. I shall say that persons who so reason are guilty of having committed the **fallacy of meaning variance**.

Thus not only is the theory of meaning employed by those who use the meaning variance argument for non-derivability false, the very importance placed on meaning for the identity of hypotheses is misplaced, and thus the fundamental argument is invalid.

3. Theoretical Identities, Concepts, and Meaning

There is another argument which deserves attention because it seems to lie just below the surface in so much of the discussion of meaning and reduction. It goes like this:

(i) All important scientific change involves a change in our concepts.

(ii) Our concept of an **x** is the meaning of the word "**x**".

(iii) So a change in any concept is a change in meaning.

(iv) Thus all important scientific change involves a change in meaning.

This is applied to a particular case in the following way:

(a) The Einsteinian revolution involves a change in our concept of space.

(b) Our concept of space is the meaning of the word "space".

(c) So a change in our concept of space involves a change in the meaning of the word "space".

(d) Thus the Einsteinian revolution involves a change in the meaning of the word "space".

The arguments are simple, direct, and seem to be sound.

Appearances notwithstanding the arguments are defective. They are guilty of the fallacy of equivocation.

The trouble spot is the idea of a concept. Our concept of a concept is far from being a paradigm of philosophical clarity, so one may justifiably wonder if one ought to do battle on this ground. We have no choice in this case because the battle has been brought to us. We have just enough understanding of "concept" for the argument to grab hold of us. We must therefore deal with it on its own terms. To play the onus game here (placing the onus on the arguer to provide an explanation of "concept") is merely to postpone a discussion, and involves an element of dishonesty since we do have enough understanding for the argument to be persuasive.

However we understand "concept", it does seem that important scientific change has involved a change in our concepts. The history of these changes is recorded in books with titles like **Concepts of Space**, **Concepts of Force**, and **From Atomos to Atom: The History of the Concept Atom**. Einstein changed our concepts of space and time; Maxwell changed our concept of light; Darwin changed our concept of a species; and so on. But what was it they did when they did this? They made us believe, on the basis of the superiority of their theories, that a new theoretical identity was true, and that the old one (if there was one) was false. Whereas we used to believe that space is a three dimensional Euclidean continuum, we now believe, on the basis of the superiority of the general theory, that space is but three dimensions of a four dimensional Riemannian continuum, the fourth dimension being time. Whereas we used to believe that light is a wave of an unknown nature, we now believe on the strength of Maxwell's theory that it is electromagnetic radiation of certain wave lengths. That is, these theories changed our beliefs about the **nature of** space, time, light, and so on. These beliefs are theoretical identities about space, time, light, and so on.

What sorts of things are theoretical identities? Saul Kripke has shown that they are identities which if true are necessarily true and if known are known **a posteriori**. [24] He did this in the following way: an expression is a rigid designator if, when it is used, it designates the entity in all possible worlds. For example, "heat" rigidly designates heat, and "molecular motion" rigidly designates molecular motion. Theoretical identities have rigid designators occurring on both sides of the identity sign. (I realize there are formally superior ways of expressing this, because the relational predicate need not occur in the middle of the names of the relata, but they are less intuitive ways.) Thus if a theoretical identity is true, the rigid designators rigidly designate the **same** entity in all possible worlds. So there is no possible world in which the theoretical identity is false, that is, it is necessarily true. To continue the example, if "heat is molecular motion" is true, "heat" and "molecular motion" designate the **same** property in all possible worlds. So there is no possible world in which the identity is false, that is, it is necessarily true.

Theoretical identities are rarely, if ever, analytic, that is, the

24 Kripke, "Naming", pp. 314-342; Saul Kripke, "Identity and Necessity", in **Identity and Individuation**, ed. Milton K. Munitz (New York: New York University Press, 1971), pp. 158-64.

expression occurring on one side of the identity is seldom, if ever, synonymous with the expression occurring on the other side. "Heat" is not synonymous with "molecular motion"; "lightning" is not synonymous with "electrical discharge from cloud to cloud or from cloud to planetary body"; nor is "gold" synonymous with "element of atomic number 79". Indeed since such statements as "Heat is molecular motion" always seem to be substantial one may think they are never analytic. It would be a mistake to close off this possibility, however, because if a theoretical identity is thought or believed to be true for some time, the use of the expressions involved may change in conformity with the identity. (Because definitions are supposed to tell us what a thing is.) In such an event one will be more inclined to say the expressions are synonymous, and so that the identity is analytic. I can think of no cases where usage **has** been changed so much that one can say outright that a theoretical identity has become analytic — "Water is H_2O" may be a candidate, though not an unproblematic one — but I can think of no reason why this should not happen. For this reason, it would be a mistake to say that no theoretical identities are or can be analytic. (The alternative is to say that what is a theoretical identity at one time may not be at another — and this is artificial.) And to say all of this is to say that the expressions involved in the identity statements need not retain (but almost always do retain) their previous semantic commitments, which commitments need not be identical. It should be noted that this entails a slight change in Kripke's view, in that it must be changed to read: if known, theoretical identities are **initially** known **a posteriori**.

In sum, the nature of the concepts about which I am now writing is described by theoretical identities; which identities are necessarily true, if true, initially known **a posteriori**, if they are known, and are usually synthetic. So when an important scientific change involves a change in our concept, we have given up one theoretical identity in favor of another. We have not necessarily, and rarely if ever, changed the meaning of a word. We certainly have not changed the meaning of any word by merely coming to favor one theoretical identity rather than another. If any change in meaning occurs, it occurs later due to a change in use influenced by the acceptance of the theoretical identity. But even this does not usually occur. This is the character of conceptual change in important scientific change.

But there is another kind of conceptual change. Philosophers in particular have used "concept of **x**" synonymously with "the meaning of '**x**'" (where "**x**" is used to refer to **x**). To grasp the concept of relativity, on this use of "concept", is to grasp the meaning of the word "relativity". To change our concept of relativity, on this use, is to change the meaning of the word "relativity".

Thus the argument under consideration involves a **non sequitur**. In particular it is an instance of the fallacy of equivocation, with "concept" being the culprit. It is probably true that all important scientific change involves a change in our concepts. This means they involve a change in our favored theoretical identities. It does not mean any meaning has changed. On the other hand, it is true that a change in concept in another sense of that word **does** involve a change in meaning. We cannot infer that all important scientific change involves a change in meaning from these two facts.

As I stated at the outset, I believe reasoning of this form lies just below the surface in much of the discussion of meaning and reduction. For example, in a passage to which I shall return later, Feyerabend says: "The relation between the thermodynamic concept of temperature and what can be defined in the kinetic theory, therefore, can be seen to conform to the pattern that has been described at the beginning of the present section: we are again dealing with two incommensurable concepts." [25] The falsity of the meaning invariance thesis is taken to follow. But "what can be defined in the kinetic theory" is not a matter of definition at all (in the relevant sense), it is a theoretical identity which says that the temperature is the mean kinetic energy of the constituent molecules. From the change in concept involved in accepting this theoretical identity, Feyerabend infers a change in meaning of the word "temperature". This is an instance of the fallacy I have in mind; it involves confusing a change in theoretical identities with a change in meaning, under the cover of our concept of a concept.

Thus the case **against** the derivability thesis has three fundamental defects in its structure: the incompatibility fallacy, the fallacy of meaning variance, and a fallacy of equivocation. But to show this is not to show that the derivability thesis is true. Nothing less than a consideration of particular cases will do that. But before turning to the particular cases, I shall discuss one important component of intertheoretical relations — the idea of the limiting case. Often the less comprehensive theory is a limiting case of the more comprehensive theory. It is important therefore to be clear about the nature of the limiting case relation. I discuss it now to make the discussion of the particular cases clearer.

---

25 Feyerabend, "Explanation, Reduction", p. 78. A similar shuffling back and forth occurs with Norwood Russell Hanson's discussion of the concept of an electron in **Patterns of Discovery** (Cambridge: Cambridge University Press, 1961), p. 123.

4. On the Logic of the Limiting Case

In the limit where $\hbar \to 0$, the laws of quantum mechanics must reduce to those of classical mechanics.[26]

The branch of optics which is characterized by the neglect of the wavelength, i.e. that corresponding to the limiting case $\lambda_o \to 0$, is known as **geometrical optics**.[27]

These statements and others like them are fairly common in physics and astronomy. Their logic is not as obvious as their prevalence would indicate.

I shall argue that there are three common ways of backing such statements:

(i) **The Mathematical Limiting Process** - Here one uses the limiting operation on the laws (axioms, equations, hypotheses, principles or postulates; hereafter just "laws") of the more comprehensive theory. For example David Bohm writes:

> Note also that as $v/c \to 0$ (which is equivalent to letting $c \to \infty$), the Lorenz transformation reduces to $z' = z - vt$, $x' = x$, $y' = y$, $t' = t$ which is just the Galilean transformation. In this way we see definitely that the older concepts of space and time are contained in those of Einstein, as special limiting cases, applicable when v/c is not too large.[28]

Essentially Bohm begins with a Lorentz transformation, for example

$$z' = (z\text{-}vt)/ \sqrt{1\text{-}(v^2/c^2)}$$

Then taking the limit as $c \to \infty$

$$\lim_{c \to \infty} z' = \lim_{c \to \infty} ((z\text{-}vt)/\sqrt{1\text{-}(v^2/c^2)})$$

and making use of the familiar theorems of limits on the right hand side he obtains

$$\lim_{c \to \infty} z' = z\text{-}vt$$

which says that in the limit as $c \to \infty$, $z' = z\text{-}vt$ which is the corresponding Galilean transform.

This method has been used to show that classical mechanics is a limiting case of quantum mechanics (as $\hbar$ [Planck's constant] $\to 0$ or n [quantum number] $\to \infty$) and that classical thermodynamics is a limiting case of statistical thermodynamics (as N [the number of degrees of freedom] $\to \infty$).[29]

The propriety of this procedure has recently been questioned, so it is worthwhile looking into the objection. It has

26 Albert Messiah, **Quantum Mechanics**, Vol. 1 (Amsterdam: North-Holland, 1961), p. 214.

27 Max Born and Emil Wolf, **Principles of Optics**, 3rd revised ed. (Oxford: Pergamon Press, 1965), p. 109.

28 David Bohm, **The Special Theory of Relativity** (New York: W.A. Benjamin, 1965), p. 65. Also see: James L. Anderson, **Principles of Relativity Physics** (New York: Academic, 1967), p. 156; Georg Joos, **Theoretical Physics**, 3rd ed. (New York: Hafner, 1958), p. 242.

29 For example, L.D. Landau and E.M. Lifshitz, **Quantum Mechanics: Non-Relativistic Theory**, 2nd ed. revised and enlarged (Oxford: Pergamon Press, 1965), p. 20; and Richard C. Tolman, **The Principles of Statistical Mechanics** (Oxford: Oxford University Press, 1938), p. 633.

been argued that "letting numerical constants change value is mathematically illegitimate", on grounds that if that is allowable, then we can let a number like 2 vary:

And by these means every equation reduces to every other — a complete trivialization of the concept of intertheoretic reduction. Any physical-constant coefficient can be eliminated by taking it to 1 (take additive factors to zero). Any expression whatever may be introduced or eliminated from any equation by these means.[30]

This will not do. When physicists treat constants as if they were variables, they do so because the magnitude of the constant in question is so like the limiting value relative to the dimensions of the problem of interest. Planck's constant is so small for most ordinary purposes that its actual value is negligible for those purposes. The velocity of light is so large relative to other velocities one usually deals with that it might as well be infinite.[31] So the physicist is not approving logically of the practice of letting **any** constant go to any value.

Second, and more importantly, numerical constants have the value they have in the empirical sciences contingently. That is, it is a matter of contingent fact that $h = 6.63 \times 10^{-34}$ joule-sec. In another possible world it might have another value. And it is this fact that makes it legitimate to treat it **as if it were** a variable. To treat it as a variable is not to be committed to the statement that it is a variable. Clearly, if one was so committed one would be guilty of inconsistency and so of failing to make mathematical sense. Numbers, on the other hand, are not constants. More important, numbers are not the sorts of things that have a value. They may be, if you like, the value of something or the other, but they do not for all that have a value. Hence they cannot even be treated **as if** they were variables. Thus it makes no sense to speak of letting the number 2 vary, though it does make sense to treat a physical constant as if it were a variable. So letting numerical constants change value is mathematically legitimate.

To summarize: in the mathematical limiting process one begins with a law of theory **T**:

1. $A = B$

where B contains the limiting "variable" **x**, that is, $B = ...x....$ Then one takes the limit of both sides of the law

2. $\lim_{x \to n} A = \lim_{x \to n} B$

---

30 Nickles, "Two Concepts", p. 199. Also, in this rather strange ending to an otherwise clear and helpful article, it is claimed (without argument) that it makes no physical sense to let $h \to 0$ or $c \to \infty$. But somehow, in spite of the fact that it makes neither mathematical nor physical sense, it is illuminating to do so (p. 201). It is difficult to see how something which purports to make mathematical as well as physical sense but does neither can be illuminating.

31 One should keep in mind those "definitions" of "infinity" that natural scientists often have in mind, e.g. indefinitely large.

where **n** is a number. One then uses the familiar theorems on limits to obtain

$\lim_{x \to n} A = B'$

where $A = B'$ is a law of **T'**. One has thereby shown that a law of **T'**, namely $A = B'$, is a limiting case of a law of **T**, namely $A = B$. And by carrying this out for all the fundamental laws of **T'** one has shown that **T'** is a limiting case of **T**.

(ii) **Contrary to Fact Assumption** - Here one makes an assumption which is contrary to the assumptions of the more comprehensive theory or contrary to empirical fact or both in order to derive the laws of the less comprehensive theory from the more comprehensive. [32] About special relativity and classical mechanics, for example, Pauli wrote:

> . . . it is to be noted that [$x' = (x-vt)/\sqrt{1-\alpha v^2}$, $t' = (t - \alpha vx)/\sqrt{1-\alpha v^2}$] contains the transformation formulae of ordinary mechanics $x' = x - vt$, $t' = t$, which can be obtained by putting $\alpha = 0$. Following P. Frank, these latter are now generally given the name "Galilean transformations." It is obvious that, by putting $c = \infty$, they can equally well be derived from [$x' = k (x - vt)/\sqrt{1 - (v^2/c^2)}$ and $t' = k(t-(v/c^2)x)/\sqrt{1 - (v^2/c^2)}$]. [33]

Here one starts with the Lorentz transform

$x' = x - vt/\sqrt{1 - (v^2/c^2)}$

Then one assumes that the velocity of light is infinite, i.e.

$c = \infty$

which is contrary to fact. It is also assumed that $1/\infty = 0$, so

$v^2/c^2 = 0$

Thus one obtains the Galilean transform

$x' = x - vt$

This method has been used to show that classical mechanics is a limiting case of quantum mechanics (with the assumption

---

32 The key assumption in the derivation of quantum theory from the hidden variable theory of Bohm is an example of the first type. To derive quantum theory one assumes that the nonlinearities are zero. This is incompatible with the fundamental assumption of the hidden variable theory that the fundamental equations are nonlinear (David Bohm, "A Suggested Interpretation of the Quantum Theory in Terms of 'Hidden' Variables", I, II, **Physical Review**, 85 (January, 1952) 166-79, 180-93). That nature is linear may not be false as a matter of empirical fact. The classical mechanics-special relativistic case to be discussed is a case in which the assumption ($c = \infty$) is contrary to fact, but not to the theoretical principle of the more comprehensive theory. Most of the commonly known assumptions fall in the category of being contrary to the assumptions of the more comprehensive theory as well as to experimental fact, for example the assumption that Planck's constant equals zero. In all of these examples I am assuming that what is derived and what is commonly identified as the less comprehensive theory **is** the less comprehensive theory. I will make good on the assumption later. The point here is to characterize the nature of the assumptions on the basis of which the alleged derivations are carried out. Thus whether the product of the derivation actually **is** the theory alleged is immaterial here.

33 W. Pauli, **Theory of Relativity** (Oxford: Pergamon Press, 1958). Also see: H. Minkowski, "Space and Time", in **The Principle of Relativity** (New York: Dover, 1923), pp. 78-79; Albert Einstein, **Relativity: The Special and the General Theory,** 15th ed., enlarged (London: Methuen, 1959), p. 33; Max Born, **Einstein's Theory of Relativity**, revised ed. (New York: Dover, 1962), pp. 246, 267.

that $\hbar = 0$), that thermodynamic relations are limiting cases of kinetic theoretical relations (assuming the number of molecules, n $= \infty$), that thermodynamics is a limiting form of statistical mechanics (assuming that the number of systems, n $= \infty$ or that the fluctuations are zero), and that special relativity is a limiting case of general relativity (assuming the region to be dealt with is infinitely small).[34]

The more mathematically inclined may have severe qualms about letting the velocity of light c, or the number of particles or degrees of freedom of a canonical ensemble n, equal an infinite number, not because c and n are in fact finite, but because it involves treating "∞" as the name of a number, for example, treating $1/\infty$ as being equal to zero when it is undefined. Allowing this contradicts the Archimedian axiom. So it is illegimate in standard arithmetic and analysis.

However, treating infinity as a number in this way has been practiced in theoretical physics for many years as the quote and the texts cited in the accompanying footnote show. Even more recent and more mathematically sophisticated works such as the recent tome on gravitation by Misner, Thorne and Wheeler do this.[35] Indeed some applied mathematics texts are equally guilty or innocent.[36] So if we are concerned to show the working logic of the physicist, we are perfectly within our rights and duty to point this out.

But second and more important, the ideas of infinite and infinitesimal numbers have recently been shown to be perfectly legitimate.[37] The late Abraham Robinson has shown that " whatever our outlook and in spite of Leibniz' position, it appears to us today that the infinitely small and infinitely large numbers of a non-standard model of analysis are neither more nor less real than, for example, the standard real numbers."[38] Robinson proved this by extending the real number system, R, to *R which includes infinite as well as infinitesimal numbers.

34 For example, Messiah, **Quantum Mechanics**, Vol 1, p. 214; Eugen Merzbacher, **Quantum Mechanics** (New York: John Wiley & Sons, 1961), p. 3; Boltzmann, **Gas Theory**, pp. 310, 318, 320, 321 (but see p. 11); David Ruelle, **Statistical Mechanics: Rigorous Results** (New York: W.A. Benjamin, 1969), p. 11; Peter Fong, **Foundations of Thermodynamics** (New York: Oxford University Press, 1963), pp. 78, 80, 92; Albert Einstein, "The Foundation of the General Theory of Relativity", in **The Principle of Relativity** (New York: Dover, 1928), p. 118.

35 Charles W. Misner, Kip S. Thorne, and John Archibald Wheeler, **Gravitation** (San Franciso: W.H. Freeman, 1973), pp. 414-15, 596, 597, 607.

36 J.W. Mellor, **Higher Mathematics for Students of Chemistry and Physics** (New York: Dover, 1955), p. 13.

37 I am indebted to Dr. Frank Papp for much help in what follows. However he is not responsible for the views expressed. In fact he disagrees with much that I have to say.

38 Abraham Robinson, **Non-Standard Analysis** (Amsterdam: North-Holland, 1966), p. 282. Also see: Martin Davis and Reuben Hersch, "Nonstandard Analysis", **Scientific American** 226:6 (June, 1972) 78-86; Abraham Robinson, "Standard and Nonstandard Number Systems", **Nieuw Archief voor Wiskunde**, 21:3 (1973) 115-33.

The new numbers are then called "real numbers" and the familiar reals are called "standard real numbers". A number is infinite if it is greater than every standard real. A number is infinitesimal if it is less than every positive standard real. Since every non-zero real number has a multiplicative inverse and an infinite number, ∞ , is non-zero, it too must have a multiplicative inverse namely, 1/∞ which is a positive infinitesimal. [39] So mathematical sense has been given to the idea of an infinite number being a divisor of a finite number. Second, the standard part of a real number *r is the standard real r if *r is infinitely close to r. So physicists who assume 1/∞ = 0 can be interpreted as taking the standard part of the positive infinitesimal 1/∞ which is zero.

I do not mean to suggest that anyone has anything like a complete theory of infinite divisors for it does not exist yet. But such a theory may not be very far off. In his presidential address to the Association for Symbolic Logic, Robinson called for more work to be done in this area: "It would be of great interest to produce a (mathematical or metamathematical) framework in which the infinite divisors of a number field can be considered more uniformly on a par with the finite divisors." [40] In any case, there is enough to show that sense can be given to the activities of the physicists.

This is another instance in which physicists have jumped beyond the mathematical frontier only to have mathematical "civilization" come creeping up sometime later. (Another recent instance of this is the Dirac delta function. [41]) Physicists have thought themselves justified in thinking of ∞ and infinitesimals as numbers on grounds of convenience and physical significance. Treating them as numbers made things easier mathematically speaking. Physically, ∞ is thought of as an indefinitely large magnitude, so large that when it is in the denominator and finite terms appear in the numerator the term is in effect and for all intents and purposes zero. [42] Now they know they were on firmer ground than they thought.

These qualms dealt with we may summarize the method of

39 A.H. Lightstone, "Infinitesimals", **The American Mathematical Monthly** 79:3 (March, 1972) 244.
40 Abraham Robinson, "Metamathematical Problems", **The Journal of Symbolic Logic** 38 (September, 1973) 512.
41 Max Jammer, **The Conceptual Development of Quantum Mechanics** (New York: McGraw-Hill, 1966), pp. 313-14.
42 For example, see: J. Willard Gibbs, **Elementary Principles in Statistical Mechanics** (New York: Dover, 1962), pp. 74, 75, 104, 105, 166. The fluctuation of the energy about the mean value is of the order of $1/\sqrt{n}$ where **n** is the number of particles in the sample. So if there are an infinite number of particles in the sample, the fluctuation of the energy is zero. In this event the mean values become the only values and one gets classical thermodynamics. More will be said of this in section 5.5.

contrary to fact assumption as follows: one begins with a law of theory **T**

    1. A = B

where B contains the limiting "variable" x. Then one supposes, contrary to fact or assumed fact that

    2. x = n

where n is a number. This assumption is subject to conditions to be discussed in section 7. One then derives a law of **T'**

    A' = B'

One has thereby shown that the law of **T'** is a limiting case of a law of **T**. By carrying this out for all the fundamental laws of **T'** one has shown that **T'** is a limiting case of **T**.

(iii) **Negligibility Assumption** - Here one assumes that the limiting "variable" is negligibly small compared to other magnitudes involved. From this assumption and the more comprehensive theory one derives the less comprehensive theory. That the "variable" is negligibly small is sometimes true, so this method does not belong in the contrary to fact category. That it is true when and where it is accounts for the success of the less comprehensive theory. That it is false when and where it is accounts for the failure of the less comprehensive theory and thus for the greater accuracy of the more comprehensive theory.

I shall use the classical-relativistic mechanics case as an example again. Max Born wrote:

> Particular interest attaches to the limiting case in which the velocity v of the two systems becomes very small in comparison with the velocity of light. We then arrive directly at the Galileo transformation. . . . For **if v/c can be neglected** in comparison with 1, we get from [the Lorentz transformation]
> $$x' = x - vt, y' = y, z' = z, t' = t$$
> Thus we understand how, on account of the small value that v/c has in most practical cases, Galilean and Newtonian mechanics satisfied all requirements for some centuries.[43]

Again one begins with a Lorentz transform

$$x' = x - vt/\sqrt{1 - (v^2/c^2)} \tag{1}$$

and the assumption that

$$v/c \text{ is negligible} \tag{2}$$

Then

$$v^2/c^2 = 0 \tag{3}$$

so

$$x' = x - vt \tag{4}$$

43 Born, **Einstein's Theory**, pp. 237-38, underline is mine. Another good example of this comes from the work on gravitation by Misner, Thorne and Wheeler: "Newtonian mechanics is recovered from the mechanics of special relativity in the mathematical correspondence limit in which all relevant velocities are negligibly small compared to the velocity of light." (**Gravitation**, p. 412). Also see: J.L. Synge, **Relativity: The Special Theory**, 2nd ed. (Amsterdam: North-Holland, 1965), pp. 113-14; Richard C. Tolman, **Relativity, Thermodynamics, and Cosmology** (Oxford: Clarendon Press, 1934), p. 21.

which is the Galilean transform.

This is not quite right for strictly one must imagine universal quantifiers in front of (1), (3) and (4). This means that strictly (2) ought to read:

Suppose v/c is **always** negligible (2′)

Clearly this is contrary to fact and the failure of Newtonian mechanics shows it to be so.

But this is not to say that the contrary to fact assumption must always have universal quantifiers. The schema here instantiated with special relativity is quite compatible with the statements' in question having indefinite scope. In this situation the assumption could be indefinite in scope, as in (1) - (4). [44]

One might be inclined to argue that (2) could be true and (3) strictly speaking false, so (3) does not follow from (2), and one has not deduced the Galilean transform from the Lorentz. This objection will not work for the force of "strictly speaking" is just to cancel the hypothesis that v/c is negligible. To speak strictly in this context is just to say that nothing is negligible.

This method has been used to show that classical mechanics is a limiting case of quantum mechanics (assuming the finite value of h is negligible) and that geometrical optics is a limiting case of physical optics (assuming that the wave length λ is negligible.) [45]

Schematically: one begins with a law of theory **T**,

1. A = B

where B contains some magnitude **m**, i.e. B = ...**m**.... One then supposes that

2. **m** is negligible

which is subject to conditions to be discussed in Section 7. One then derives a law of **T′**

A′ = B′

whereby one has shown that the law of **T′** is a limiting case of a law of **T**. Again if one does this for all the fundamental laws of **T′** one shows that **T′** is a limiting case of **T**.

These are, then three commonly occuring ways of backing a claim that one law is a limiting case of another. All involve standard deductive techniques. All involve the derivation of the limiting case and not some approximation to it. That is, expressions of the form A = B are derived, and not expressions

---

44 See: Ronald M. Yoshida, "Von Neumann's Proof and Hidden Variables" (unpublished Ph.D. dissertation, University of Washington, 1971), pp. 194-203.

45 Merzbacher, **Quantum Mechanics**, p. 4; P.A.M. Dirac, **The Principles of Quantum Mechanics**, 4th ed. (Oxford: Clarendon Press, 1958), p. 122; Edwin C. Kemble, **The Fundamental Principles of Quantum Mechanics** (New York: Dover, 1958), pp. 50, 51; Robert B. Leighton, **Principles of Modern Physics** (New York: McGraw-Hill, 1959), p. 107; Born and Wolf, **Optics**, p. 109.

of the form $A \simeq B$ or $A = B \pm \delta$. [46] The derivation shows of course that the limiting case is approximately true but to say that is not to say that what is derived is an approximation. Finally it is understood that the claim that all involve derivations of a law of the less comprehensive theory will only be fully vindicated when particular cases have been discussed in greater detail. It is to that task that I shall now turn.

5. The Particular Cases

In this section I shall discuss the arguments that have been advanced in various cases for one particular theory's not being derivable from another. In each case I shall argue that the conclusion is false, that is, I shall argue that the less comprehensive theory **is** derivable from the more comprehensive theory. Where meaning variance arguments have been given, I shall do this by merely indicating how the usual putative derivations go (since these are never questioned by the meaning variance theorists) and by arguing for the identity of the result of the derivation with a fundamental law of the less comprehensive theory (which **is** questioned by the meaning variance theorists). I shall discuss these theory pairs in rough historical order, because what is the more comprehensive theory in one pair may be the less comprehensive theory of a later pair, and this will save repetition of exposition.

5.1 Impetus Theory and the Mechanics of Newton

Feyerabend has argued that we cannot derive the "inertial law" of the impetus theory from the mechanics of Newton. [47] The "inertial law" of the impetus theory says

The impetus of a body in empty space which is not under the influence of any outer force remains constant. [48]

The impetus is by definition (and here Feyerabend's will do):

...the force responsible for the movement of an object that has ceased to be in direct contact, by push, or by pull, with the material mover. [49]

The basis for Feyerabend's claim is that (i) "impetus" "cannot be defined in a reasonable way within Newton's theory", [50] and (ii) it cannot be empirically related to any property in Newton's theory. [51] Since, according to Feyerabend, these are the only ways "impetus" could occur in the mechanics of Newton, it cannot occur there, and so Buridan's "inertial law" is not derivable.

This will not do for the simple reason that Buridan's

46 Contrast with: Putnam, "How Not to Talk About Meaning", p. 207.
47 Feyerabend, "Explanation, Reduction", pp. 52-62.
48 **Ibid.**, p. 54.
49 **Ibid.**, p. 55. See: Marshall Clagett, **The Science of Mechanics in the Middle Ages** (Madison: University of Wisconsin Press, 1959), pp. 534-35.
50 Feyerabend, "Explanation, Reduction", p. 57.
51 **Ibid.**, p. 58.

impetus can be identified with Newton's inertia. (It does not matter to me whether one calls such an identification a definition, or one says there is another way "impetus" might occur in Newton's mechanics — just so long as none of the facts are overlooked.) Newton conceives inertia to be a force which is identical in kind to the impetus of Buridan. In definition III Newton wrote:

> The **vis insita** or innate **force** of matter, is a power of resisting, by which every body, as much as in it lies, continues in its present state, whether it be of rest, or of moving uniformly forwards in a right line . . . t his **vis insita** may, by a most significant name, be called inertia (**vis inertiae**) or **force** of inactivity.[52]

And in definition IV, the definition of impressed force, he said:

> For a body maintains every new state it acquires by its inertia only.[53]

Clearly, the inertia of Newton is the impetus of Buridan. (It should be mentioned here to prevent misunderstanding that inertia is a different kind of force from that involved in the second law.)[54]

We can see, then, that the "inertial law" of the impetus theory can be derived from the mechanics of Newton, in particular from the first law of Newton (the inertial law) and the identity "impetus = inertia".[55]

5.2 **Kepler's Laws and Newtonian Mechanics**

It seems to be accepted as a truism these days that Kepler's laws are incompatible with Newtonian mechanics and gravitational theory and so cannot be derived from them.[56] Here we have a very clear instance of the incompatibility fallacy. The mistake was apparently started by Pierre Duhem who had the following in mind: Since the Newtonian law of universal gravitation says that **every** body attracts every other body in the solar system, and since there is more than one planet in the solar system, the other planets must attract any given planet as well as the sun. Given this fact, the orbits must not be perfect ellipses with all that that entails. So Kepler's laws are incompatible with Newton's laws,[57] and if they are

52 Isaac Newton, **Mathematical Principles**, Vol. 1, trans. Andrew Motte, rev. Florian Cajori (Berkeley: University of California Press, 1962), p. 2. Second and fifth underline is mine.
53 **Ibid**.
54 For this point see: Jammer, **Force**, p. 120.
55 It should be mentioned that Feyerabend commits both the incompatibility fallacy and the fallacy of meaning variance in his discussion. See, "Explanation, Reduction", p. 59.
56 For example, Carl G. Hempel, "Deductive-Nomological **vs**. Statistical Explanation", in **Minnesota Studies in the Philosophy of Science**, Vol. 3, ed. Herbert Feigl and Grover Maxwell (Minneapolis: University of Minnesota Press, 1962), p. 101; Hempel, "Reduction", p. 190; Mary Hesse, **The Structure of Scientific Inference** (London: Macmillan, 1974), p. 26; Nagel, "Issues", p. 120; Sklar, "Types", p. 111.
57 Pierre Duhem, **The Aim and Structure of Physical Theory** (New York: Atheneum, 1962), pp. 191-92.

incompatible, they must not be derivable.

This bit of reasoning has the same defects as the case of free fall discussed in section 1. Newton's and Kepler's laws are not incompatible **by themselves**. Any alleged incompatibility must be brought out with the aid of other assumptions, for example, that there are other bodies in the solar system. But no statement incompatible with Kepler's laws can be deduced if we insist that these other assumptions be strictly true. (Recall: such assumptions carry with them the tacit assumption that these are the only physically relevant considerations [p.6]). This is shown by the fact that strict truth would require us to account for all other eight planets, their satellites, the various asteroids, space junk and the comings and goings of various comets, not to mention every other body in the universe, every electron, every proton, etc., all of which involves us in the **n** body problem — which problem has no general solutions. Morever what solutions there are involve all manner of approximation. One involves "throwing the four inner planets into the sun", that is, adding their mass to that of the sun. So if we insist on the strict truth of the assumptions, we cannot even derive an approximation to Kepler's laws which is incompatible with them. And if we do not insist on the strict truth, but allow the auxiliary assumptions to be approximately true, then the fallacy has been clearly committed, for there is no way to block the derivation of incompatible propositions from a theory plus turn by turn two sets of assumptions both of which are approximately true.

If we allow the assumption that the masses of, say, space junk, asteroids, satellites and the other bodies in the universe are negligible, then we should also allow the assumption which is used in the standard derivations of Kepler's laws that the masses of the other planets in the solar system are negligible. To be sure one approximation seems better than the other but even that one would not hold for some purposes, nor would it hold if a sufficiently massive body came near the solar system. And if we allow the assumptions to be made, there is no logical barrier to our **deriving** propositions which are incompatible by the use of different sets of auxiliary assumptions.

The only relevant barrier one might imagine at this stage of the argument is a referential barrier. But there is no doubt that the referents of the main descriptive terms which occur in both theories are identical. That is, "planet", "Mars", "sun", etc., "ellipse", "period", and so on refer to the same entities in both theories. Even Sklar, who commits the incompatibility fallacy, says of this pair that "the concepts of the reduced are certainly a subset of the concepts of the larger theory".[58]

Thus it is clear that if statements which are syntactically identical to those of Kepler's laws are derivable from Newtonian mechanics plus the appropriate auxiliary assumptions, they **are** Kepler's laws, and not some look alikes. And this derivation occurs in just about any text on mechanics as an example of a central force problem, and in any celestial mechanics text as an introduction to planetary theory. The usual way the derivation is accomplished is to derive the second law (that the radius vector sweeps out equal areas in equal times) from the law of gravitation and the second law of motion plus the assumption that the masses of the other planets are negligible. Then one can derive the first law (that the orbits of the planets are elliptical), with the aid of the additional assumption that the velocity of the planet at any point of its orbit is less than its escape velocity. Finally, the third law (that the square of the period of a planet is proportional to the cube of the mean distance from the sun) is derived with the aid of the additional assumption that the arithmetic mean between the two diameters of the elliptical orbit is a little less than the longer diameter because the eccentricity is so small, which was also assumed by Kepler.[59]

5.3 Galileo's Law and Newtonian Mechanics

It has also become commonplace to hold that Galileo's law is not derivable from Newton's laws.[60] I discussed this case in section 1 to illustrate the incompatibility fallacy. I did not mention there how the derivation is carried out. The reader will recall that the alleged incompatibility came from the fact that g, the acceleration due to gravity, is a constant in Galileo's law for freely falling bodies, whereas it varies with the height above the surface of the earth according to Newton's theory plus certain assumptions, which it was shown involve approximations. Galileo's law, **with g appearing as a constant** is also derivable from Newton's theory plus certain other assumptions, in particular, the assumption that the height above the surface of the earth is negligible relative to the radius of the earth. Since it is usually assumed by both parties (deductivists and non-deductivists) that the radius of the earth is constant, the distance between the centers of mass is a constant; so g, the acceleration due to gravity, is a constant. By integrating the

58 Sklar, "Types", p. 111.
59 Johann Kepler, **The Laws of Planetary Motion**, selection included in **The Origins and Growth of Physical Sciences**, Vol. 1, ed. D.L. Hurd and J.J. Kipling (Harmondsworth: Penguin Books, 1964), p. 132.
60 Feyerabend, "Explanation, Reduction", pp. 46, 47; Hempel, "Reduction", p. 190; Kenneth Schaffner, "Approaches to Reduction", **Philosophy of Science** 34:2 (June, 1967) p. 139; Sklar, "Types", p. 111.

resulting equations of motion one gets $s = \frac{1}{2} gt^2$, Galileo's law.

5.4 **Physical Optics and Electromagnetic Theory**

In his well known article ''Approaches to Reduction'', Kenneth Schaffner argues for the non-derivability of physical optics from electromagnetic theory:

> The conclusion that can be drawn from these examples is that what Maxwell's theory entails is a theory of physical optics which bears close relations to the earlier theory of physical optics — but which certainly is not identical to it.[61]

Schaffner gives three ostensible grounds for this claim. I shall discuss each in turn.

> (1) In the first place we need suitable reduction functions which will identify light waves with electromagnetic waves of a certain frequency range, and the electric vector with the light vector.[62]

This point cuts no logical ice. No one denied that we need ''reduction functions'' to reduce (or deduce) physical optics to (from) electromagnetic theory. If the point is merely that one cannot derive physical optics from Maxwell's equations alone, the point is made, but at the cost of making the claim irrelevant to the literature on the subject. A glance at Nagel and Feyerabend shows that they differ on the derivability of the reduced theory from the reducing theory plus the **appropriate assumptions** (see the discussion in section 1).

> (2) Even with these appropriate reduction functions, we will discover that some reduction instances are exact, whereas others are not — i.e., are only approximate. Snell's law comes out without change, but the Fresnel ratios have an additional factor in them when they are derived from Maxwell's theory which does not appear in them originally. The corrective effect of the factor is small, but significant, for it tells us that the behavior of light is dependent on the magnetic properties of the medium through which it passes.[63]

What he has in mind is given in a footnote:

> The original Fresnel ratios are $A_{refl.}/A_{incid.} = \sin(i-r)/\sin(i+r)$; the expression deducible from Maxwell's theory, after using the appropriate reduction function is:
> $A_{incid.}/A_{refl.} = 1/2 . [1 \pm (\mu_1/\mu_2) . (\sin i \cos r/\sin r \cos i)]$
> [Here he cites Sommerfeld's **Optics**, (**Lectures on Theoretical Physics**, Vol. 4, New York: Academic, 1954, p. 16), which reduces to the above simpler form if $\mu_1 = \mu_2$.)[64]

61 Schaffner, ''Approaches'', pp. 141-142.
62 **Ibid.**, p. 141.
63 **Ibid.**, p. 142.
64 **Ibid.**

This is making too much of something which is, in a way, an accident. It is an accident or idiosyncracy (see below) that Sommerfeld deduced that expression, **then** made the additional remark that when $\mu_1 \sim \mu_2$ "which usually obtains" we get the original Fresnel ratio. If he had started with the assumption that $\mu_1 = \mu_2$, approximately true though it may be, the original Fresnel ratio would have fallen out. Schaffner's view seems to be based on a rather limited look at texts on optics for a glance at other texts shows that the assumption $\mu_1 = \mu_2$ is made first, then the Fresnel ratio is deduced from it.[65] The advantage of doing it this way is obvious; assuming the truth of the electromagnetic theory, the derivation shows the conditions under which the Fresnel ratio holds. It follows that **the** Fresnel ratios are derivable, that is, Schaffner's claim is false.

The only way he can save his claim is to say that $\mu_1 = \mu_2$ is not part of Maxwell's theory. But to do this is to pay too high a price for salvaging this thesis. It is an obvious fact that in order to apply Maxwell's equations or any other set of fundamental laws to a kind of phenomenon, certain assumptions must be made about the character of the phenomenon. Even the Fresnel-like expression Schaffner says is deducible from Maxwell's equations is deducible only with the aid of the assumptions that we have at least two media each of which has a different dielectric constant, that they meet at an interface, etc. So Schaffner could save his claim only by claiming that little or nothing is derivable from Maxwell's equations or any other fundamental theory. While this is true in a sense, it is hardly worth pointing out, since the literature indicates authors were aware of this and the debate on derivability was being carried out on the assumption that one was speaking of the derivability of one theory from another **plus** the appropriate assumptions.

(3) In the late 19th century, there were a number of theoreticians attempting to solve the problem of diffraction by a black screen—A screen which absorbs all the light which falls upon it. It turns out that this concept of a "black screen" is impossible to define in the context of electromagnetic theory since: "the property 'black' cannot be defined by boundary conditions within the realm of Maxwell's theory. Therefore diffraction by a black screen cannot be formulated as a boundary value problem."[66] (The quotation is from Sommerfeld, **Optics,** p. 266.)

65 C.L. Andrews, **Optics of the Electromagnetic Spectrum** (Englewood Cliffs: Prentice-Hall, 1960), p. 399; Born and Wolf, **Optics,** p. 38; Paul Drude, **The Theory of Optics** (New York: Dover, 1959), p. 269; Joos, **Theoretical Physics,** p. 350; R.K. Luneberg, **Mathematical Theory of Optics** (Berkeley: University of California Press, 1966), p. 72; and finally and most important, Maxwell himself makes such an assumption and argues for it before he does anything else: James Clerk Maxwell, **A Treatise on Electricity and Magnetism,** Vol. 2 (New York: Dover, 1952), p. 437.
66 Schaffner, "Approaches", p. 142.

The thrust is clear: "black screen" can be defined in physical optics; it cannot be defined in Maxwell's electromagnetic theory; therefore physical optics is not derivable from Maxwell's theory.

Sommerfeld may have been right. Blackness may not be definable by boundary conditions in Maxwell's theory.

Schaffner, however, is wrong. The concept of a black screen is definable in Maxwell's theory.[67] The problem of a black screen is not a boundary value problem, it is a saltus problem, that is, one which has to do with a discontinuity, in this case, a discontinuity in the light function. F. Kottler defined "black screen" by making use of a non-physical space into which the light travels "as through an open door...where it loses itself at infinity".[68] This device is akin to that of the representation of virtual images by using a non-physical space, a technique, I might add, which was introduced by Sommerfeld (Schaffner's authority). In fact it is the antithesis of that technique. In that theory, reflected light comes out of the non-physical space (and never goes in) after being reflected by the virtual object. In Kottler's theory light goes into the space but never comes out.[69]

With that, Schaffner's case for the non-derivability of physical optics from electromagnetic theory vanishes.

Worse yet, the conclusion is false: physical optics is embodied in the wave equation, and the wave equation is derivable from Maxwell's equations plus certain assumptions, namely (i) that the electromagnetic field one is dealing with has no charges or currents; (ii) that the constitutive or material relations are true — in particular, that the electric displacement is equal to the product of the dielectric constant and the electric vector, that the magnetic induction is equal to the product of the magnetic permeability and the magnetic vector; (iii) that the medium is homogeneous; (iv) $v = c/\epsilon\mu$ where v is the wave velocity, c is the velocity of light, ϵ is the dielectric constant, and μ the magnetic permeability; and finally (v) the theoretical identity that light is electromagnetic radiation in the frequency range from approximately $4 \times 10^{14} \text{sec}^{-1}$ to 7.5×10^{14} sec^{-1}, and that the light vector is identical to the electric vector for those frequencies.[70] The theoretical identity (v) guarantees that the vector function in the equation that results refers to the light wave — the same thing that was referred to by the light

67 F. Kottler, "Diffraction at a Black Screen; Part I: Kirchoff's Theory", in **Progress in Optics**, Vol. 4, ed. E. Wolf (Amsterdam: North-Holland, 1965), pp. 283-314; and F. Kottler, "Diffraction at a Black Screen; Part II: Electromagnetic Theory" in **Progress in Optics**, Vol. 6, ed. E. Wolf (Amsterdam: North-Holland, 1967), pp. 333-77.
68 Kottler, "Electromagnetic Theory", p. 348.
69 Kottler, "Kirchoff's Theory", p. 303.
70 For the derivation see, for example, Born and Wolf, **Optics**, p. 1-11.

vector of physical optics. Since all that remains are operators that mean the same in both equations, the equations are identical (by the criterion of identity of section 2). It follows that physical optics is derivable from Maxwell's theory.

5.5 Thermodynamics and Statistical Mechanics

Feyerabend and more recently Gordon G. Brittan have argued that "temperature" and "entropy" mean different things in thermodynamics and statistical mechanics.[71] Non-derivability is taken to follow. While it has been demonstrated that meaning variance is not sufficient for non-derivability, it is worth discussing the particular arguments, not only because they have gone unchallenged, but because the description of the particular case is almost always more persuasive than argumentation in general terms. Hence left unchallenged these arguments will weaken the case for the irrelevance of meaning variance to these matters.

Feyerabend's argument turns on a putative definition of a temperature ratio, $T':T'' = Q':Q''$, for a substance operating between two levels L' and L'' via reversible processes. Inspection of the "established usage" of "temperature" so defined shows that it is independent of the material of the substance chosen for the cycle and unique.[72] This proposition about temperature, in conjunction with the "definition", implies the phenomenological second law of thermodynamics. No dynamical concept has that property. Second, the statistical account "allows for fluctuation of heat back and forth between the two levels of temperature and, therefore, contradicts one of the laws implicit in the 'established usage' of the thermodynamic temperature."[73] Hence, "temperature" cannot mean the same in both theories, and derivation is impossible.

A quick glance at Fermi's well known text on thermodynamics, which is cited by Feyerabend, shows that $T':T'' = Q':Q''$ is not a definition at all. It is a theorem derived from the first and second laws.[74] Second, to argue from the claim that there is no dynamical concept which entails the "strict (i.e. nonstatistical) second law" when it is applied to concrete situations is to beg the question, for the question just is whether statistical mechanics entails the second law. Third, under the limiting conditions (the only conditions under which it is claimed that classical mechanics is derivable) the fluctuations are zero, so heat cannot fluctuate back and forth between two levels of temperature. Let me illustrate this point

71 Feyerabend, "Explanation, Reduction", pp. 77-78; Gordon G. Brittan Jr., "Explanation and Reduction", **Journal of Philosophy** 67:13 (July 9, 1970) 452-53.
72 Feyerabend, "Explanation, Reduction", p. 77.
73 **Ibid**., p. 78.
74 Enrico Fermi, **Thermodynamics** (New York: Dover, 1936), pp. 42, 43.

with the energy. The fluctuation of the energy, $\overline{(\Delta E)^2}/\bar{E}^2 = kT^2C_v/\bar{E}^2$ (k is Boltzmann's constant and C_v is the heat capacity), turns out to be of the order of $1/\sqrt{N}$ where N is the number of particles in the sample. For example, a perfect monatomic gas has $\bar{E} = (3/2)NkT$ and $C_v = (3/2)Nk$, so $\Delta E/E = \sqrt{2/(3N)}$. Thus in the limit of an infinite number of particles, the fluctuation of the energy is zero. In this event the mean values become the only values.

This talk of a limit has been taken in all three senses outlined in section 4. Tolman and Khinchin used the mathematical limiting process; Boltzmann and Fong used the contrary to fact assumption, and Gibbs, the negligibility assumption.[75] Fong's case is interestingly different from the rest, because he in effect assumed at the outset that the fluctuations are zero in order to get classical thermodynamics. Whichever method one uses, the fluctuation vanishes and with it Feyerabend's case.

Brittan and Feyerabend also argue for the meaning variance of "entropy". Brittan, for example, says:

> The statistical mechanical analogue of the classical concept of entropy, to pick but one example, goes well beyond it in that it has a meaning in nonequilibrium situations, as contrasted with the classical situation in which nonequilibrium states are, on a number of assumptions, converted to equilibrium states in terms of which empirical temperature [entropy?] is defined.[76]

Brittan's (and Feyerabend's) claim is false for all the major accounts of the reduction of thermodynamics with which I am familiar. Where it is true, it is irrelevant. I shall illustrate this with the treatments of Fowler and Tolman.

Fowler "defines" (this is actually a theoretical identity or what is sometimes called a "quantitative definition") "entropy" by $S = k \log C$ where S is the entropy, k is Boltzmann's constant, and C is "the number of complexions belonging to states which differ only insignificantly from the equilibrium state".[77] A "complexion" is an accessible state of unit weight, that is, it is a state which is compatible with the given conditions (e.g., the total energy) and which is given unit weight for statistical purposes. It is clear that this "definition" is meaningless for nonequilibrium conditions in general (since C is the number of complexions of states close to equilibrium) though it can be extended, as can the classical "definition", to

75 Tolman, **Statistical Mechanics**, p.633; A.I. Khinchin, **Mathematical Foundations of Statistical Mechanics** (New York: Dover, 1949), p. 156; Boltzmann, **Gas Theory**, pp. 310, 318, 320, 321; Fong, **Foundations**, pp. 79, 80, 92; Gibbs, **Statistical Mechanics**, pp. 74-75, 104.

76 Brittan, "Explanation and Reduction", p. 452; also see: Feyerabend, "Explanation, Reduction", p. 78.

77 R.H. Fowler, **Statistical Mechanics** (Cambridge: Cambridge University Press, 1966), p. 189.

cover those non-equilibrium states which can be converted to equilibrium states.[78]

Tolman used a different procedure. At equilibrium, $S = -k\bar{\bar{H}}$, where k is Boltzmann's constant and $\bar{\bar{H}}$ is a complicated function which corresponds to the **exact** probabilities for energy states in the canonical ensemble which represents equilibrium. This is the entropy for a system in thermodynamic equilibrium and it is not applicable to non-equilibrium situations.[79] This, of course, is the entropy which is required for the derivation of thermodynamics.

This idea has been generalized to cover nonequilibrium situations as $S = -k\bar{\bar{H}}$, where $\bar{\bar{H}}$ is now a complicated function which corresponds to "coarse **grained**" probabilities of a group of states.[80] A "coarse grained" probability is the mean of fine grained or exact probabilities taken over neighboring states of nearly identical properties. Here S is the entropy of **any** system. This is meant to cover all situations.[81] It is obvious that this generalized entropy is the entropy Brittan and Feyerabend had in mind, for it applies to nonequilibrium states. And it is equally obvious that the fact that **this** generalized entropy applies to all situations is irrelevant to the discussion both of meaning variance and derivability, for it is the nongeneralized entropy of the previous paragraph that is used in the derivations of thermodynamics.

So the only relevant use of "entropy" in statistical mechanics does not apply to nonequilibrium situations. Thus Brittan has established no contrast with the use in classical thermodynamics, and he has no case for meaning variance.

One might be inclined to argue that the identification of the entropy as a function of the exact probabilities for energy states itself is sufficient to establish a difference of meaning, since the identification could not be made in classical thermodynamics. That this will not do has been established in section 3. In theoretical identities words retain their previous semantic commitments (at least initially and usually indefinitely). So no meaning change follows from the mere occurrence of the identity.

Thus not only has it been shown that meaning variance does not imply nonderivability (the fallacy of meaning variance), no meaning variance has been shown.

Another argument has been advanced in Feyerabend's name. J.J.C. Smart says classical thermodynamics and

78 **Ibid.**, p. 204. Also see: Gregory H. Wannier, **Statistical Physics** (New York: John Wiley & Sons, 1966), pp. 83-87 for a Gibbsian approach which has the same features.
79 Tolman, **Statistical Mechanics**, p. 538.
80 **Ibid.**, p. 460.
81 **Ibid.**, p. 539.

statistical mechanics are inconsistent, hence one cannot be derived from the other.[82] What he had in mind is that "from the standpoint of statistical thermodynamics Brownian movement can be shown to imply violations of the second law of thermodynamics (fluctuations involving temporary **decreases** of the entropy of a system)".[83]

The statistical description of Brownian motion requires certain auxiliary assumptions in addition to the postulates of statistical mechanics. These auxiliary assumptions involve many contrary to fact or negligibility assumptions.[84] The alleged derivation of classical thermodynamics also requires auxiliary assumptions which are contrary to fact or negligibility assumptions. Since it is quite possible that the postulates in conjunction with the different sets of auxiliary assumptions should entail incompatible results, the incompatibility in no way entails that the one result is derivable while the other is not. There simply is no legitimate basis for this asymmetry in treatment. This is another clear case of the incompatibility fallacy discussed in section 1.

In short none of the arguments in the literature show nonderivability. Crucial premises are false, or the very inferences themselves are fallacious.

In addition, and this is the most important result, classical thermodynamics **is** derivable from statistical mechanics. Obviously I cannot do it here, but I can indicate how by dealing with the controversial points here and referring the reader to the relevant texts for the mathematical details. Among the postulates of statistical mechanics we have: (i) the quantum theory as the underlying mechanical theory and (ii) the assumption of equal **a priori** probabilities for different regions in phase space (that is, the assumption that the phase point of a system is just as likely to be in one region of the phase space as in any other region which is compatible with existent knowledge of the system). In addition to these postulates we need the following auxiliary assumptions in order to derive the second law: (iii) the increase in the energy of a system that accompanies the absorption of heat from the surroundings is the main increase in the internal energy of the members of the statistical ensemble, and the heat absorbed from the surroundings is the mean energy transferred from heat reservoirs; (iv) the thermodynamic systems to be dealt with are in equilibrium; (v) the equilibrium state is to be represented by a quantum canonical ensemble; (vi) the probabilities are

82 J.J.C. Smart, **Between Science and Philosophy** (New York: Random House, 1968), p. 79.
83 **Ibid.**, pp. 82-83.
84 Albert Einstein, **Investigations on the Theory of the Brownian Movement** (New York: Dover, 1956), **passim**.

normalized; (vii) the entropy is the mean value of the degree to which the condition of the system deviates from its equilibrium value; (viii) the temperature is the mean kinetic energy; and finally, in order to derive the strict second law, (ix) there are an infinite number of particles.[85] In order to obtain the first law all one needs to add to (iii) is the assumption that the work done on the surroundings is the mean work done on the external bodies by the members of the ensemble.

The use of these particular assumptions must of course be justified. Assumptions (iii), (vii), and (viii) are theoretical identities, justified antecedent to the derivation by appeal to the fact that the mechanical properties referred to on the right hand side of the identities (with the exception of the mean heat) have the same properties that the properties named on the left hand side have, that is, they enter into the same or similar kinds of relations.[86] Their ultimate acceptance rests on the acceptance of the theory (the **a posteriori** character of theoretical identities).

Assumption (iv) is made because classical thermodynamics is an equilibrium theory. And (v) is justified by showing how the canonical distribution can deal with situations like those encountered in thermodynamics.[87] Assumption (vi) is simply a normalization condition, i.e. one imposed to make the probabilities make sense. And since thermodynamic systems are composed of indefinitely many systems, assumption (ix) is for most intents and purposes approximately true. When this assumption breaks down for other intents and purposes, the classical laws also break down.

These postulates conjoined with these auxiliary assumptions entail a statement which is expressed with the sentence "$\Delta S \geqslant \int \delta Q / kT$". In the meaning variance arguments for nonderivability the main bone of contention is the identity of this statement. It is argued that this sentence does not express the second law of classical thermodynamics because "S" and "T" in it do not mean the same as they do in the sentence which is used to express the classical law. We have seen many times over the irrelevance of meaning to the identity of the results. What matters is the reference. And on this score few would deny that "T" or "temperature" refer to that property which is a measure of the intensity of the heat or that "S" refers to that property which is a measure of the unavailable

85 These are essentially the assumptions employed by Tolman, **Statistical Mechanics**, chaps. 9 and 13. Also see: Gregory H. Wannier, "Quantum-Mechanical Proof of the Second Law", **American Journal of Physics** 33.3 (March, 1965) 222-25.

86 Tolman, **Statistical Mechanics**, pp. 538-58; Gibbs, **Statistical Mechanics**, pp. 168-69.

87 **Ibid.**, pp. 498-506, 530-33.

energy **in both classical thermodynamics and statistical mechanics**. Since neither the identity of the referent of "Q" nor the referents of the mathematical symbols are questionable, the sentence "$\Delta S \geq \int \delta Q/kT$" is used to express **the** second law of classical thermodynamics and not merely a likeness to it. That is, the second law of classical thermodynamics **is** derivable from statistical mechanics.

And since there are no unique problems with the first law, classical ("strict", "phenomenological" to use Feyerabend's adjectives) thermodynamics **is** derivable from statistical mechanics.

5.6 **Classical Mechanics and Special Relativity**

At least three arguments have been given which purport to show that classical mechanics cannot be derived from the special theory. All are arguments from meaning variance and so straightway are guilty of committing the fallacy of meaning variance. But here as in the case of thermodynamics and statistical mechanics, arguments from the particular case may be more persuasive than attacks upon general principles. Hence I shall examine these arguments in detail.

The first argument I shall consider comes from the well known article "Problems of Empiricism".[88] There Feyerabend argues that mass in the special theory is a **relation** "involving relative velocities between an object and a coordinate system, whereas [in the classical theory it] is a **property** of the object itself and independent of its behavior in coordinate systems".[89] Thus "mass" is supposed to mean something different in the two theories.

The inadequacy of this argument starts to become clear when one considers the fact that a relation is a property of an object as well and furthermore a property can be conceived of as nothing more than a unary relation. That is, there is no essential difference between the two. When it was found that gas pressure is a function not only of the temperature and volume but also of the molecular dimensions and the nature of the molecular interaction, the meaning of the word "pressure" did not change in any plausible sense of the word. Yet one moved from considering pressure to be a three termed relation (a function of two variables, T and V) to considering it a five termed relation (a function of four variables, T, V, a, b). One was simply mistaken in believing pressure depended only on the temperature and volume. Similarly, and for that reason, when it was found that the mass varied with the velocity of the object relative to the frame of interest, the word "mass" need not have undergone any change. Essentially one moved from

88 Feyerabend, "Problems", pp. 168-70.
89 **Ibid.**, p. 169.

considering mass a one termed relation to considering it a three termed relation, that is, a function of the rest mass and the velocity of the object relative to the frame of interest. To put this in the material mode, we can consider the special theory as saying that the mass (the same mass of which the Newtonians spoke) varies with the velocity of the object. That is, the different theories simply make incompatible claims about one and the same property of a body. So nothing about meaning change follows from any of this.

Feyerabend's second argument occurs in "Against Method".[90] There he claims that the conceptual system connected with the terminology of classical mechanics

> . . . assumes that the properties [of shape, speed and mass] **inhere** in objects and that they change only if one interferes with the object, not otherwise. The theory of relativity teaches us at least in one of its interpretations, that there are no such inherent properties in the world, neither observable nor unobservable, and it produces an entirely new conceptual system for description inside the domain of mechanics.[91]

It is a little difficult to get one's hands on this argument because it is not clear what inherent property is being talked about. Certainly having mass is as inherent a property of objects in the special theory as it is in classical mechanics — few would dispute this. Second, the property of having a particular mass $m (= m_0/\sqrt{1 - (v/c)^2})$ is at least as inherent a property of an object moving with a velocity v relative to the reference frame of interest, S, as having a particular mass m is in classical physics. In what sense, then, does the theory of relativity teach us that there is no such inherent property as mass? Not in the sense that an object may have different masses at **different** times, for that is also true in classical mechanics, for example, the mass of burning rocket fuel changes in time. Then perhaps it is that according to special relativity an object may have different masses at the **same** time. According to the theory the same object may have the mass $m' (= m_0/\sqrt{1 - (v'/c)^2}$ at t relative to frame S' and may have mass $m'' (= m_0/\sqrt{1 - (v''/c)^2}$ at t relative to frame S" where $m' \neq m''$. So saying that an object has the mass m' and m" at t is merely an elliptical way of saying that it is moving with a velocity v' relative to S' and a velocity v" relative to S" at t and that mass is a function of the velocity. That mass is a function of velocity is an inherent property, as has already been indicated. That an object has different velocities relative to

90 P.K. Feyerabend, "Against Method: Outline of an Anarchistic Theory of Knowledge", in **Analyses of Theories and Methods of Physics and Psychology**, Vol. 4 of **Minnesota Studies in the Philosophy of Science,** ed. Michael Radner and Stephen Winokur (Minneapolis: University of Minnesota Press, 1970), pp. 81-82.
91 **Ibid.**, p. 82.

different frames is not. But the fact that an object's having a particular velocity is not an inherent property of that object no more shows that any property dependent on the velocity in general, like the relativistic mass, is not inherent, than having different masses at different times shows that properties dependent on mass, like having a kinetic energy, are not inherent.

Second, even if classical theory assumed that mass is an inherent property and the special theory claimed that it is not, it would not show that "mass" means something different in the two theories. Chomsky assumed that the property of knowing certain restrictive principles of universal grammar is an inherent feature of the mind. Some of Chomsky's critics hold that it is not an inherent feature. Still no one would say on that account that "knows certain restrictive principles of universal grammar" means something different to the two parties. So difference in assumptions or claims even when they are about inherent properties does not show difference in meaning.

Similar criticisms can be raised against Feyerabend's similar claims about shape and speed. And with that his argument collapses.

Thomas Kuhn has argued for meaning variance on different grounds. According to Kuhn, the variables and parameters that occur in the Newtonian look-alike statements which **are** derivable from the postulates of the special theory refer to Einsteinian space, time, and mass. The variables and parameters that occur in Newton's laws, of course, refer to Newtonian space, time, and mass. This would not cut any philosophical ice if Einsteinian and Newtonian space, time, and mass were identical, but they are not, for Newtonian mass is conserved; Einsteinian is not. Thus while the variables and parameters are the same their meanings are not. So the Newtonian look-alike statements cannot be Newton's laws. Newton's laws are not therefore derivable from the special theory. [92]

This is persuasive, but unsound. The whole argument turns on the supposition that the variables and parameters of the special theory refer to Einsteinian space, time, and mass, while those of Newtonian mechanics refer to Newtonian space, time and mass. This supposition is false. Take "mass" or "m". Einsteinian mass is that mass which obeys the laws of special relativity; Newtonian mass is that mass which obeys Newton's laws. If "mass" in Newtonian physics refers to that mass which satisfies Newton's laws, then its obeying those laws must be a necessary or contingent characteristic of the referent. It cannot

92 Kuhn, **Revolutions**, pp. 101-2.

be a necessary characteristic because if it were, Newton's laws and their consequences would be self-referring, necessary, analytic, and **a priori** as we have seen. But they are none of these. That Newton's second law, which is the best candidate to have these properties, is not self-referring is, I hope, clear. That the second law is not necessary is shown by the Atwood machine. The Atwood machine consists of two masses m_1 and m_2 attached to the end of a massless thread which is run over a frictionless and massless pulley. Newton's second law and the law of universal gravitation entail that $a = g(m_2\text{-}m_1)/(m_2 + m_1)$. Now suppose the law of gravitation is true and that $a \neq g(m_2\text{-}m_1)/(m_2 + m_1)$. Then $F = ma$ is false in that possible world. In that world it might be that $F = ma^{1.5}$ or $F = ma + E/\phi$ where E is the energy and ϕ is the longest dimension of the body. That the second law is not analytic is shown by considering the fact that force is a cause, acceleration an effect, and the product of the mass and acceleration is a physical magnitude. Neither of the latter is of the right category to be identified with force. The product of the **measures** of the mass and acceleration may be equal or identical to the **measure** of the force, indeed that is what the law says, but that is not to say that **force** is identical to the product or that "force" means "product of...". The measure of a person's height may be equal to a measure of his employability (to within a constant), but for all that no one would think that "height" means the same as "employability". Nor would one want to say that "measure of the force" means (is synonymous with) "measure of the product of the mass and acceleration". That the second law is not known **a priori** is shown by the fact that we do not know **a priori** if the predictions regarding the Atwood machine are true or not. Further, we have good reason for believing the third law (since we are really considering the whole theory and not merely the second law) is strictly speaking false and so **a fortiori** not **a priori**. I have in mind the case of two charges moving in arbitrary directions towards one another. The instantaneous forces acting on the charges are not equal and opposite.[93] Again it follows that mass (as that word is used in Newtonian mechanics) does not necessarily satisfy Newton's laws.

Nor does mass contingently satisfy Newton's laws. It does not contingently satisfy the laws, because it does not satisfy those laws. This is shown by the famous Bücherer experiment which shows that mass increases with velocity. Under the **classical** (Newtonian) description of that experiment, the

93 See: Milton Rothman, **Discovering the Natural Laws** (Garden City: Double-day, 1972), pp. 41-44; Leigh Page, **Introduction to Theoretical Physics**, 3rd ed. (Princeton: D. Van Nostrand, 1952), pp. 442-43, 534-35.

charge-to-mass ratio of an electron would have to be a constant. But that is observed to be false. [94] It follows that ''m'' does not refer to the measure of that mass which obeys Newton's laws, that is, ''m'' does not refer to the measure of Newtonian mass. Likewise ''mass'' does not refer to Newtonian mass.

What about ''mass'' in special relativity? The story here is similar. If ''mass'' in the special theory refers to that mass which satisfies the laws of special relativity, then its obeying those laws must be a contingent or necessary characteristic of the referent. It cannot be a necessary characteristic because if it were, the laws of special relativity and their consequences would be self-referring, necessary, analytic, and **a priori**. They are none of these things. It cannot be a contingent characteristic because special relativistic theories of gravitational phenomena are false on observational grounds, or are inconsistent. [95] It follows that in special relativity ''mass'' does not refer to that mass which obeys the laws of special relativity, that is, it does not refer to Einsteinian mass.

With that Kuhn's argument seems to collapse. It is simply irrelevant to point out that Newtonian and Einsteinian mass are different because the parameters do not refer to them.

At this point one might be inclined to argue that I have misrepresented the nature of the respective masses, that Newtonian mass is whatever mass is referred to in Newton's laws, and the same **mutatis mutandis** for Einsteinian mass. My arguments are therefore irrelevant.

This will not do either, for now we have not one shred of good evidence that Newtonian and Einsteinian masses are different. That different claims are made shows only that **if** we construe them as being about the same characteristic, then the different theories make incompatible claims about that characteristic, and there is nothing wrong with that.

But, it may be argued, there is something wrong if the claims turn out to be **that** different. Just as two people who think they are talking about the same person may come to infer that they are talking about different persons as their descriptions diverge, so we should infer the Newtonian and Einsteinian theories are about different characteristics from the different ''descriptions'' the theories give.

But the differences are not **that** great. If we construe the common terms as having the same referents, special relativity gives **identical** explanations and predictions for the vast range of phenomena with which Newtonian theory successfully deals (under the limiting condition). That is no small matter.

94 See for example, Irving Kaplan, **Nuclear Physics** (Reading, Mass.: Addison-Wesley, 1963), p. 121.
95 Misner, Thorne, and Wheeler, **Gravitation**, pp. 177-191, especially 187-89.

Syntactically the common terms enter into identical or very similar kinds of relations. Fundamental principles are naturally called by the same names, for example, "conservation of linear and angular momentum", not to mention "Newton's second law of motion". But more than that, in the analogy the two parties can infer that they are talking about different persons, because it is presumed that they are or were in a position to tell what the person of whom they are speaking is like, that is, it is reasonable to assume the descriptions are both true. Consequently incompatible descriptions (incompatible, that is, if they are about the same person) make it reasonable to infer that the descriptions are really about different persons. That is not the situation of the two theories. One has good reason for believing both are strictly speaking false as I have already indicated. Even if we work on the level of approximations a similar situation obtains. One is a better approximation than the other, one gives more accurate predictions than the other, so one cannot treat them as if they are "equally true" and conclude they must be about different things. This tack simply will not work. It follows that Kuhn's argument will not work either.

But this raises the question about what the referent of "mass" is. In the Appendix I argue that **in both theories** "mass" refers to that property of a body in virtue of which it resists a change in motion. In outline the argument goes: An examination of the literature of classical physics shows that "mass" refers **at least** to that property of a body in virtue of which it resists a change in motion. All other properties are such that either it is false that the referent of "mass" in classical mechanics has them (e.g. the property of being conserved), or they will not do anything for the case of the meaning variance theorist, that is, they will not contrast with attributes of the referent of special relativity (e.g. "the property which classical mechanics **says** is conserved"). An examination of texts introducing special relativity shows that there too "mass" refers to that property in virtue of which a body resists a change in motion. Typically an introductory text begins with a discussion of classical mechanics. When special relativity is introduced no indication is given of a change in reference. Yet reference change is a sufficiently drastic change that an author would indicate it if he was doing it. One can only conclude that it is not being done. Thus "mass" refers to the same property (that in virtue of which a body resists a change in motion) in both theories, and "m" refers to a measure of that property.

This suggests that Newtonian mechanics is derivable from special relativity, contrary to the critics of Nagel. The suggestion is borne out when one considers that in both theories "$\vec{F}$" refers to a vectorial quantity which is a measure of that which causes a change in motion and which acts in the direction of motion (this latter is not true for force in the special theory except under the limiting assumption, $c = \infty$ or v/c is negligible). Second, $d^2\vec{r}/dt^2$ refers to the acceleration of the body whose mass is m in both theories.

Now $\vec{F} = m d^2\vec{r}/dt^2$ is derivable from the postulates of the special theory plus one of the limiting assumptions. (The only putative grounds for denying this that I have seen are that the equation, or Newtonian mechanics in general, is incompatible with the special theory. But to so argue is to commit the incompatibility fallacy.) The equation in question says that the magnitude and direction of that which causes a change in motion of a body is equal to the product of the magnitude of that property of the body in virtue of which it resists a change in motion and the acceleration of a body which runs in the direction of the force. This is exactly what the second law of motion of Newtonian mechanics says, hence the equation **is** the second law.

The first law of motion (the principle of inertia) is embodied in the idea of an inertial or Galilean reference frame in the special theory; an inertial or Galilean frame just is one in which the principle of inertia holds. [96]

The third law of motion (the principle of action and reaction) is derivable from the principle of relativity and the principle of the constancy of the velocity of light. From these two principles one can obtain the homogeneity of space. [97] From the homogeneity of space one can derive the conservation of momentum, [98] and from that plus the assumptions of two particles with an "internal impulse (of attractive type) shuttling to and fro between them" [99] and the infinite velocity of the internal impulse (the contrary to fact assumption) or the negligibility of terms of the order of $1/c^2$ (the negligibility assumption) one can derive the third law. [100]

Thus Newtonian mechanics can be derived from special relativity.

5.7 Classical Celestial Mechanics and the General Theory of Relativity

In order that terms should have a stable meaning in the transition from classical celestial mechanics to the general

---

96 Einstein, **Relativity**, pp. 11, 13, 19, 20.

97 Cornelius Lanczos, **Space Through the Ages** (New York: Academic, 1970), pp. 231-32.

98 Kenneth W. Ford, **The World of Elementary Particles** (New York: Blaisdell, 1963), p. 109.

99 Synge, **Special Theory**, p. 254.

100 **Ibid.**, pp. 253-58, by combining equations (245) and (240) and eliminating Wl_e/r.

theory of relativity it is necessary that the transition "occurs within the extension of a more general idea of space S that was established already before the advent of [the general theory]".[101] No such general idea of space occurs in common sense or empirical science, and if it occurs in metaphysics it must be shown that the idea was shared by the defenders of classical celestial mechanics and the general theory. This has not been shown, and the metaphysics would be rejected in any case. Thus there is no such idea and so no stability of meaning. So argues Feyerabend.

There **was** a general idea of space which was "established" before the advent of the general theory, and that is of space as the indefinitely great expanse in which all material objects are located and all physical events occur. It is clear from his discussion however that this is not what Feyerabend was looking for. This is a mere description of the "local grammar" of "space".[102] What is wanted is a general theory. Whoever has this more general idea must be capable of distinguishing between topological, affine and metrical properties of space, and must not be committed to an unambiguous distinction between spatial and temporal properties (whatever that means).[103] Further he must not retain (as Riemann did) an overall Euclidean topology, and must appreciate the contribution of time to the metric.

It is difficult if not impossible to see why such a general theory is required for the stability of meaning and why the earlier description of the "local grammar" would not do — unless one is already committed to Feyerabend's theory of meaning (which was refuted in section 2). But I shall not pursue this point any further. It will be sufficient to show that there was such a general idea amongst pre-(general)-relativistic physicists and mathematicians.

It is clear that the mathematics of such a space had been developed prior to the general theory.[104] Riemannian geometry and the tensor calculus had been developed in the nineteenth century. Nineteenth century scientists could distinguish topological, affine, and metrical properties of space.[105] Further, the generalized idea of space of Riemann did not retain a Euclidean topology, for spherical and elliptical spaces are special cases of the generalized space and they are

---

101 Feyerabend, " 'Meaning' ", p. 179.
102 **Ibid**., p. 178.
103 **Ibid**.
104 Morris Kline, **Mathematical Thought from Ancient to Modern Times** (New York: Oxford University Press, 1972), pp. 1130-31.
105 **Ibid**., pp. 906, 918, 1164.

inconsistent with a Euclidean topology. [106] And as near as I can understand the expression, Lorentz was not committed to an "unambiguous distinction between spatial and temporal properties":

> It had, however, already become clear from Lorentz's earlier work that some of the transformations must involve not only x, y, z but also the variable t. So . . . he now replaced the condition of transforming $(x^2 + y^2 + z^2)$ into itself by the condition of transforming the expression $(x^2 + y^2 + z^2 - c^2 t^2)$ into itself. . . . [107]

This also shows he appreciated the contribution of time to the metric.

So the "general idea of space" that Feyerabend requires for stability of meaning existed prior to general relativity, and the transition to general relativity occurred "within the extension of a more general idea of space S that was established already before the advent of [general relativity]". With that nothing is left of this argument for meaning variance.

Feyerabend gives a second argument for meaning variance in his "Reply to Criticism". Here his argument is that

> The fact that within [general relativity] all events are embedded in a four-dimensional Riemannian continuum which acts not merely as a somewhat unusual background of coordinates, but is supposed to describe **intrinsic properties** of physical processes now necessitates the reformulation of all the basic laws of [classical celestial mechanics] and the redefinition of all its basic concepts (spatial distance; temporal distance; mass; force; etc.) [108]

Feyerabend illustrates and justifies this claim with the cases of mass and distance:

> The classical, or absolute idea of mass, or of distance, cannot be defined within (the general theory). Any such definition must assume the absence of an upper limit for signal velocities and cannot therefore be given within [the general theory]. [109]

And he generalizes this into:

> Not a single primitive descriptive term [of classical celestial mechanics] can be incorporated into [the general theory]. [110]

---

106 Max Jammer, **Concepts of Space** (New York: Harper & Brothers, 1960), p. 149. Riemann did not retain a Euclidean topology in his beliefs about physical space as Feyerabend claims, for he thought questions about immeasurably large areas, and so **a fortiori** about the whole of unbounded space, useless. (See: Bernard Riemann, "On the Hypotheses which Lie at the Foundations of Geometry", in **A Sourcebook in Mathematics**, Vol. 2, ed. David Eugene Smith [New York: Dover, 1959], p. 423.)

107 Sir Edmund Whittaker, **A History of the Theories of Aether and Electricity**, Vol. 2: **The Modern Theories 1900-1926** (New York: Harper & Brothers, 1960), p. 32 (also see pp. 31-35 and Vol. 1, p. 406).

108 Feyerabend, "Reply", p. 231.

109 **Ibid**.

110 **Ibid**.

Feyerabend's failure to indicate in any way what he takes to be a definition in this argument makes the argument difficult to evaluate. We often think of definitions as reports of usage. Yet what philosophers call theoretical identities are called definitions by scientists, for example, "temperature is the mean kinetic energy" is sometimes said to be a definition. And theoretical identities are not usually reports of usage; the expressions on either side of the identity sign usually retain their prior distinct semantic commitments (see section 3 above).

If "definition" is construed so that theoretical identities count as definitions, the Riemannian continuum used in the general theory **does** require "redefinition" of the basic concepts of classical celestial mechanics. When the putative derivation of classical celestial mechanics (in particular the law of gravitation) is undertaken (i) the referent of the variable "x^1" of the general theory is identified with the referent of "x" in the standard formulations of Newtonian mechanics; the referent of "x^2" is identified with that of "y"; the referent of "x^3" with "z"; and the referent of "x^4" with "ct". (ii) A weak, static gravitational field is assumed (that is, a gravitational field is assumed for which the components of the metric tensor, the g_{ik}, do not change with time; are negligibly different from -1 for $i = k = 1,2,3$; are negligibly different from $+ 1$ for $i = k = 4$; and are negligibly different from 0 for $i \neq k$). It is assumed that (iii) the velocity of light is infinite or that terms of the order of $1/c^2$ are negligible. And (iv) the Newtonian gravitational potential is identified with the metric coefficient, g_{44}:

['$d^2x^\sigma/d(x^4)^2 = -(1/2) (\partial g_{44}/ \partial x^\sigma)$', which has been derived from the relativistic free particle equation and (ii)] can easily be rewritten in a form familiar in the Newtonian theory of gravitation if we introduce our usual spatial and temporal variables by their relation with Galilean coordinates
$$x^1 = x \quad x^2 = y \quad x^3 = z \quad x^4 = ct$$
and **define** the Newtonian potential ψ in terms of g_{44} by the expression

$$\psi/c^2 = (g_{44}/2) + \text{constant}$$
or
$$\psi/c^2 = (g_{44} - 1)/2 \qquad g_{44} = 1 + (2\psi/c^2). \text{ [111]}$$

These assumptions imply that space is flat, i.e. that it is Euclidean. Mass is still that property of a body in virtue of which it resists a change in motion. Gravitational mass is still that mass which is the source of the gravitational field. Force is still the physical agent which causes a change in momentum. So by using (i), (iii) and (iv) and substituting for g_{44} in the

111 Tolman, **Relativity**, p. 199, underline is mine.

equation, we get the Newtonian law of gravitation in the more familiar form:

$$d^2x/dt^2 = -\partial\psi/\partial x, \quad d^2y/dt^2 = -\partial\psi/\partial y, \quad d^2z/dt^2 = -\partial\psi/\partial z.$$

So if theoretical identities count as definitions for Feyerabend, the Riemannian continuum used in the general theory does require "redefinition" of the basic concepts of classical theory. **But**, such "redefinition" does not exclude incorporation of the "primitive descriptive terms" of the classical theory, indeed it initially requires it as I have argued in section 3 above. So, far from entailing a meaning change, the use of the Riemannian continuum requires semantic stability.

On the other hand, if "definition" is construed so that theoretical identities do **not** count as definitions, then the classical or absolute idea of mass or distance may not be "definable" within the general theory, that is, we may or may not be able to find an expression with exactly the same sense; but that is not needed to derive the classical theory. All one needs is the assumed truth of the theoretical identities (i) and (iv) in the above and the assumptions (ii) and (iii). A simple model will show this. In order to derive (in the sense discussed in section 1 above) "x is P" from "x is S", "P" need not mean the same as "S"; it will do if S = P, that is, if the property of being S is the property of being P. It is in virtue of these identities that one knows that the equations one obtains are the classical equations.

To summarize: if "definition" is so used that theoretical identities count as definitions, the basic terms of classical celestial mechanics need to be "redefined", but far from entailing meaning variance, the required "redefinition" requires meaning **in**variance. On the other hand, if theoretical identities are **not** to count as definitions, "redefinition" is not required to relate the theories; all one needs are the identities, and these require meaning invariance. So whichever way we cut this philosophical ice, two chunks of meaning is not the result.

To be sure, the "fact that within [general relativity] all events are embedded in a four-dimensional Riemannian continuum" does change our concept of space, and with it perhaps all the related kinematic concepts. While we used to believe that space is a three dimensional Euclidean continuum with time as an independent adjunct, we now believe that space is three dimensions of a four-dimensional Riemannian continuum with time as the fourth dimension. But as we have seen in section 3, this does not show us that the meaning of the word "space" or any of the related kinematic words has changed in meaning — to so argue is to commit the fallacy of equivocation. What has changed is our belief about the nature of space, not the meaning of the word.

I have written as if the derivation of the classical law of gravitation was sufficient to derive classical celestial mechanics, as if the laws of motion were not required. This is not so, though the law of gravitation is the most important part. But assumption (ii) regarding the weak, static gravitational field is sufficient to derive the special theory. [112] And as we have seen in section 5.6, assumption (iii) regarding the infinite velocity of light or the negligibility of terms of the order of $1/c^2$ in conjunction with the special theory is sufficient to derive the classical laws of motion. The classical theory is therefore derivable.

5.8 Classical Mechanics and Quantum Theory

In the standard discussions of the classical limit of quantum mechanics one considers a particle in a potential $V(\vec{r})$ with the modulus and phase in its wave function separated, i.e, $\psi(\vec{r}) = A(\vec{r})\exp(i/\hbar)S(\vec{r})$; one substitutes the wave function in the Schrödinger equation; then by separating the real and imaginary parts one obtains two equations:

$$(\partial S/\partial t) + ((\nabla S)^2/2m) + V = (\hbar^2/2m)(\Delta A/A), \qquad (1)$$

and

$$m(\partial A/\partial t) + (\nabla A \cdot \nabla S) + (A/2)\Delta S = 0; \qquad (2)$$

then by setting $\hbar = 0$, the right side of equation (1) vanishes and the result is taken to be the Hamilton-Jacobi equation. From this equation Newton's second law is derived in the form $md\vec{v}/dt = -\nabla V$. [113] However this is not sufficient. It must also be shown that $\vec{p} = \nabla S$, where $\vec{p}$ is the momentum, for this is necessary for S to be the characteristic function of the Hamilton-Jacobi equation. [114] This is accomplished by showing that in the classical limit, i.e., when $\hbar = 0$, A^2(or $|\psi|^2$) is the classical probability density in configuration space for a system in which the initial coordinates are not completely known, i.e., where $\rho = |A^2| = |\psi|^2$, where ρ is the classical probability density. [115] Then by multiplying equation (2) by 2A, one gets

$$(\partial A^2/\partial t) + (1/m)\nabla \cdot A^2 \nabla S = 0 \qquad (3)$$

The classical probability obeys a conservation law:

$$(\partial \rho / \partial t) + \nabla \cdot (\rho \nabla H|_{\rho = \partial S/\partial q}) = 0 \qquad (4)$$

where H is the Hamiltonian. The gradient of the Hamiltonian just is the velocity $\vec{v}$ of the particle, and since $A^2 = \rho$, equations (3) and (4) tell us that

$$\vec{v} = \nabla S/m, \text{ i.e. } m\vec{v} = \vec{p} = \nabla S \qquad (5)$$

112 Misner, Thorne and Wheeler, **Gravitation**, p. 413.
113 For example, see: Messiah, **Quantum Mechanics**, Vol 1, pp. 219-24.
114 See: Herbert Goldstein, **Classical Mechanics** (Reading, Mass: Addison-Wesley, 1959), p. 274.
115 Lowell S. Brown, "Classical Limit and the WKB Approximation", **American Journal of Physics** 40 (March, 1972) 371-76.

So S is the characteristic function of the Hamilton-Jacobi equation, and we know that

$$(\partial S/\partial t) + ((\nabla S)^2/2m) + V = 0 \qquad (6)$$

(equation (1) when $\hbar = 0$) is the Hamilton-Jacobi equation. And from this one can derive

$$m(d\vec{v}/dt) = -\nabla V \qquad (7)$$

which apparently is Newton's second law of motion.

Feyerabend has argued that this derivation does not show that quantum theory reduces to classical mechanics as a special or limiting case. [116] According to Feyerabend, any such reduction must satisfy two conditons: (i) all problems which are successfully dealt with by (non-relativistic) classical physics (classical mechanics) must be capable of being treated by elementary quantum theory without help from additional assumptions which (a) do or (b) do not involve classical ideas; (ii) quantum theory must not make any assertion that disagrees with assertions not contradicted by experience which are made by classical physics (classical mechanics) in its own proper domain. Neither of these conditions is satisfied according to Feyerabend. That the first is not satisfied is shown by the fact that some macroscopic variables like Euler angles do not seem to be definable in terms of Hermitian operators. That the second condition is not satisfied is shown by the fact that quantum theory is a linear theory, while classical mechanics is not.

This will do not for several reasons. In the first place (i) is a very unreasonable requirement. The Coulomb potential is a classical idea, but it would be unreasonable to expect that quantum theory should get along without it. It is clear then that Feyerabend only wants to put certain classical ideas in the set of classical ideas quantum theory should be able to do without. He gives us no indication how to characterise this set; the result is that for some unknown reason we cannot use the concept of an Euler angle as is.

In the second place, it is easy to see that failure to satisfy requirement (i) shows nothing about the derivability or non-derivability of classical mechanics. Suppose for the moment that quantum theory cannot get by without the help of certain classical ideas forbidden-by-Feyerabend (whatever they are). At best this would show that quantum theory is defective. It would not show that classical mechanics is not derivable from quantum theory, for it might be and is claimed that it is just because it **is** derivable that we can use the classical ideas. That

116 P K Feyerabend, "Problems of Empiricism, Part II", in **The Nature and Function of Scientific Theories,** ed. Robert G. Colodny (Pittsburgh: University of Pittsburgh Press, 1970), pp. 296-300; and P.K. Feyerabend, "On A Recent Critique of Complementarity, Part I", **Philosophy of Science** 35:4 (December, 1968) 314-21.

is, it is just because classical mechanics is derivable from quantum mechanics plus the assumption that $\hbar = 0$ that one can, on quantum mechanical grounds and when the non-zero nature of the quantum of action can be ignored, use the classical results. When the quantum of action cannot be ignored, one cannot use the classical ideas. And **if** in this situation there is no Hermitian operator corresponding to a macroscopic magnitude like the Euler angles, the problem lies with quantum mechanics, not the alleged derivability of classical from quantum mechanics. It would be problematic for quantum theory in particular, because it is taken as a fundamental postulate that "each dynamical variable that relates to the motion of the particle can be represented by a linear (Hermitian) operator".[117]

Third, it has not been shown that there is no Hermitian operator corresponding to the Euler angles. Feyerabend only speaks of the **difficulty** defining them.[118] Moreover, the claim seems to be false. Dr. E.P. Wigner (in private communication) says that if two axes of the body are specified, the operators of the Euler angles can be given. (The operator of the single Euler angle in two dimensional space in the coordinate system referring to the angular momentum $m\hbar$ has the matrix elements $\Phi_{mm'} = 2\pi\delta_{mm'}$ for $m = m'$, $\Phi_{mm'} = -2\pi i/(m-m')$ for $m \neq m'$.)

Fourth, condition (ii) is equally unreasonable. There is no good reason why quantum theory should "agree" with classical mechanics in "its own proper domain". If one derives classical theory from quantum theory plus the contrary to fact assumption $\hbar = 0$, then classical mechanics can give results which "disagree" with those consequences of quantum theory in conjunction with assumptions which are considered to be "truer". The differences should however be below the threshold set by the success of the classical results, otherwise quantum theory would not be accounting for those successes of classical theory. The logical state of affairs is analogous to the kinetic theory-ideal gas equation case discussed in section 1 of this paper. There it was shown that one can derive the ideal gas equation from the kinetic theory in conjunction with certain false assumptions (perfectly elastic collisions and dimensionless molecules). This equation "disagrees" with, for example, the real gas equation, which is a consequence of the kinetic theory in conjunction with certain assumptions which are considered "truer" or better approximations than those made in the ideal gas case. Now, the ideal gas equation holds for

117 Leonard I. Schiff, **Quantum Mechanics**, 2nd ed. (New York: McGraw-Hill, 1955), p. 41.
118 Feyerabend, "Problems, Part II", p. 297.

certain monatomic light gases like helium or argon. The real gas equation gives different results for these gases, but the differences lie below the level at which the ideal gas law is successful. If they did not, the success of the ideal gas equation at that level would indicate a defect in the kinetic theory of gases. So there is no good reason why quantum theory should "agree" with classical mechanics "in its own proper domain". They may "disagree", the only constraint placed on this "disagreement" is that if quantum theory is to be a satisfactory theory then the "disagreement" must lie below the level at which classical mechanics succeeds. In fact I think this constraint is satisfied. But whether it is satisfied or not will have no bearing on the question of derivability.

Feyerabend claims that condition (ii) is not satisfied because quantum theory is a linear theory while classical theory is not, that is, the results "disagree". This will not do because the net effect of the contrary to fact assumption that $\hbar = 0$ just **is** the loss of linearity, that is, when $\hbar = 0$, the right hand side of equation (1) vanishes and the result is the non-linear Hamilton-Jacobi equation. Thus, **given** the contrary to fact assumption, the results to do not "disagree" on the question of linearity.

Finally, these arguments of Feyerabend are weak because they do not indicate any errors in the familiar derivation which was sketched at the beginning of this section. A more concrete contribution along these lines is the article by Rosen which was cited by Feyerabend. [119]

Rosen takes the case of a free particle in one dimensional rectilinear motion. He superposes two solutions for which the right hand side of equation (1), $(\hbar^2/2m)(\Delta A/A)$, vanishes when $\hbar = 0$, and obtains a solution for which he claims the right hand term does not vanish (instead, $(\hbar^2/2m)(\Delta A/A) = p^2/2m$). He concludes that:

> Either we consider classical mechanics as the limit of quantum mechanics, which is described by (the Schrödinger equation), or by Eqs. [(1) & (2) above]; or we consider classical mechanics as characterized by Eq. (6) [above], which is not always the limit of Eq. [(1)]. In the first case we may obtain states which are superpositions of other states and which have no place in the framework of classical mechanics. In the second case we obtain only states of the kind to be expected, but then classical mechanics has to be regarded as something **essentially different** from quantum mechanics, and not a limiting case of it. [120]

119 Nathan Rosen, "The Relation Between Classical and Quantum Mechanics", **American Journal of Physics** 32 (1964) 597-600; Feyerabend, "Problems, Part II", pp. 297, 343 (footnote 18).
120 Rosen, "The Relation", p. 599.

It is taken to follow that classical mechanics is not a limiting case of quantum theory.

Several points must be made about this argument. First, the validity of the familiar derivation is limited in such a way as to exclude the free particle case of Rosen, because the derivation proceeds on the assumption that one has a particle on a potential $V(\vec{r})$. Rosen is not the only one to have overlooked this point. [121] Second, it is generally understood in the approximation that one is dealing with a well defined wave packet. Rosen's superposition case involves the superposition of two plane waves travelling in opposite directions. Cohn has argued that one can construct a well defined wave for which the $(\hbar^2/2m)$ $(\Delta A/A)$ term still does not vanish. [122] However, Donald Kobe has shown that that solution can be given an interpretation under which the term in question does vanish. [123]

Third, and I believe everyone has overlooked this, once one has equation (1), one assumes $\hbar = 0$. This means that the cases being discussed where $\Delta A/A$ involves a $1/\hbar^2$ term (to cancel the $\hbar^2$ of the coefficient) are ill-defined, hence the cancelling is meaningless. Fourth, even assuming one can make good on this, Lowell S. Brown has constructed a derivation which is good for the Schrödinger equation including terms up to order $\hbar$, thus eliminating the relevance of such cases. [124]

Finally, Rosen wrongly assumes, ''If the superposition principle holds in quantum mechanics, then it must also hold in classical mechanics if the latter is a limiting case of the former''.[125] The Schrödinger equation is linear, which entails the validity of the principle of superposition for its solutions. However, in assuming $\hbar = 0$ one eliminates the linearity of equation (1), which leads to the nonlinear Hamilton-Jacoby equation. And with that the superposition principle goes. There is nothing logically bizarre in this. We say an ellipse may have two foci; we say a circle is a limiting case of an ellipse; but we cannot say a circle may have two foci. That is, a property of the general case may drop out for a limiting case. Nor is there anything amiss in the assumption that $\hbar = 0$. True, it is the contrary of one of the fundamental statements of quantum theory, but we have seen in section 1 and the earlier parts of this section that the assumption of the contrary of a

121 Jack Cohn, ''Quantum Theory in the Classical Limit'', **American Journal of Physics** 40 (March 1972) 465.
122 **Ibid.**
123 Donald H. Kobe, ''Comments on the Classical Limit of Quantum Mechanics'', **American Journal of Physics** 42:1 (January, 1974) 73-74.
124 Brown, ''Classical Limit'', pp. 371-76.
125 Rosen, ''The Relation'', p. 597.

fundamental statement of the more comprehensive theory is characteristic of the interesting derivations.

So Rosen's criticism of the derivation misses its mark.

David Bohm (also cited by Feyerabend) has criticized the view that classical mechanics is a limiting case of quantum mechanics by arguing that quantum theoretical "concepts" presuppose the classical "concepts":

"We may conclude then that quantum theory presupposes the classical level and the general correctness of classical concepts in describing this level; it does not deduce classical concepts as limiting cases of quantum concepts."[126]

I do not believe Bohm means to deny that classical mechanics is deducible from quantum theory in the manner that has been discussed at the beginning of this section. He is denying that quantum theory can be presented in such a way that classical ideas first occur at the end of the derivation. That is, the relationship between this theoretical pair is different from that between, say, special relativity and classical mechanics. For example, in a postulational presentation of special relativity (i.e. from the postulates rather than "inductively") one need not encounter the idea of the inertial mass of an elementary particle being a constant, or the idea of mass conservation, until one carries out the derivation involved in showing that the classical theory is a limiting form of the special theory. By contrast, Bohm argues, the quantum ideas would be meaningless without an appeal to the "classical level" **from the outset**.

This does not entail the non-derivability of the classical theory. Indeed it supports it, since it would be odd if quantum theory presupposed classical mechanics, but the latter was not derivable from the former. Since it is not my purpose here to discuss all the relations that obtain between these two theories, I shall not discuss the correctness of the presupposition claim. Let it suffice here that Bohm's remarks do not exclude derivability, that on the contrary they support it.

Another critic of the limiting case view was the late Norwood Russell Hanson. Hanson argued as follows:

(i) "If [a well formed sentence] S can be used to express an intelligible statement in one context, but not in another, it would be natural to conclude that the languages involved in these different contexts were different and discontinuous."[127]

(ii) When S expresses the state of a particle in classical physics the result is an intelligible assertion; when S is

---

126 David Bohm, **Quantum Theory** (Englewood Cliffs: Prentice-Hall, 1951), p. 625.

127 Hanson, **Patterns of Discovery**, p. 151.

used to express the state of a particle in quantum physics, "the result is no assertion in that language at all". [128]

(iii) Thus "the languages are different, **logically discontinuous**". [129] "There is no logical staircase running from the physics of 10^{-28} cm. to the physics of 10^{28} light-years. There is at least one sharp break: that is why one can make intelligible assertions about the exact coordinates and momentum of Mars, but not about the elementary particles of which Mars is constituted." [130]

Hanson argues for the unintelligibility of the S of (ii) in the quantum context as follows:

> What could the assertion consist in? That a wave packet has been compressed not to a line but to a point? This cannot even be false, since one must at least have a clear concept of x to be able to use it in making false statement. Is there any clear concept of a wave packet at a point? No. [131]

The proper retort to this latter argument is that that is exactly what it means, a wave packet has been "compressed" to a point, for the effect of letting $h \to 0$ (or assuming $h = 0$) is exactly to allow us to "compress" the wave packet to a point. And there is as clear a concept of a wave packet being "compressed" to a point (as $h \to 0$) as there is of an ellipse which has been "expanded" to a circle (as b[the length of the semiminor axis] $\to$ a [the length of the semimajor axis]) or of a circle which has become a straight line (as the radius $r \to \infty$) both of which are standard mathematical concepts. What is often done in the discussion of the classical limit of the wave packet is simply to assume that the extension of the wave packet is negligible, [132] and surely **that** is also intelligible.

So the S of (ii) is intelligible in quantum physics albeit false or unwarranted (if quantum theory is true). The inclination to deny its intelligibility comes from the failure to distinguish what cannot be expressed in a language employed in a theory from what is incompatible with the principles of the theory. One might say "That is high energy music" cannot be expressed in the language employed in the special theory of relativity. But that statement is compatible with the principles of the special

---

128 **Ibid.**, p. 152.
129 **Ibid.** Actually in the passages cited, Hanson says that (i) and (ii) would **ordinarily** be conclusive evidence for (iii) (**ibid**), but since the correspondence principle is **prima facie** counterevidence, his argument turns to deal with the principle. Since I make no use of the correspondence principle I omit mention of that part of Hanson's argument (which, I might add, results in an idiosyncratic interpretation [**Patterns**, p. 156] of the principle).
130 **Ibid.**, p. 157.
131 **Ibid.**, p. 150.
132 For example see: Messiah, **Quantum Mechanics**, Vol 1, p. 52: "...in the classical approximation where one considers the extension of the wave packet to be negligible..."

theory. On the other hand, ''The velocity of light is not constant in all inertial frames'' **is** incompatible with a principle of the special theory, but it **can** be expressed in the language employed in the special theory. Similarly, if S expresses the state of a particle in classical physics, it **is** incompatible with the uncertainty principle, but it **can** be expressed in the language employed in quantum theory. And just as one might be inclined to say ''The velocity of light is not constant in all inertial frames'' is not merely false, it could not be true because it is physically impossible that it should be true; so one might be inclined to say S is not merely false or unwarranted, it could not be true because it is physically impossible that it should be true.

Even if S **were** unintelligible in the quantum context nonderivability would not be established, because (i) is false. Take the sentence ''This is harder than that''. When solids are referred to, the sentence is intelligible. When most liquids or gases are referred to, the sentence is unintelligible. So this sentence ''can be used to express an intelligible statement in one context, but not in another'', yet by no significant stretch of semantics can one say that two languages are used; **a fortiori** one cannot conclude the languages are ''different and discontinuous ones''. The analogy is quite good. As the temperature, T, decreases ''This is harder than that'' (referring to liquids), which is initially unintelligible, becomes intelligible. So one might say (assuming the unintelligibility of S in quantum theory): As h diminishes (or n increases) S which is initially unintelligible becomes intelligible.

Even if in philosophical desperation one grasped at the straws of ''the language of solids'' and ''the language of liquids'' in the analogy, the logical discontinuity would not follow. ''If this solid were heated above its melting point but below its temperature of vaporization, it would flow'' is, I suppose a statement from ''the language of solids''. From it and ''This solid has just been heated to a temperature above its melting point but below its vaporization temperature'', one can derive ''It will flow'' which is a statement from ''the language of liquids''. That is, there is no logical discontinuity, a statement from the one ''language'' is derivable from statements of the other ''language''. So this attempt to save the argument, like the others, fails.

And with that failure goes the failure of Hanson's argument.

One final objection must be considered. In the article ''On the 'Meaning' of Scientific Terms'' Feyerabend offers yet another argument for meaning variance and therefore for nonderivability and incommensurability.[133] He puts the conclusion in the form: "It is clear that the 'conservation laws' of the quantum theory share only the name with the corresponding laws of classical physics".[134] Three grounds are given. I shall discuss each separately.

(a) "[The conservation laws of quantum theory] are expressed in terms of Hermitian operators, whereas the classical laws use ordinary functions that always have some value." [135]

There is some confusion in the literature about the conservation laws. For example, different statements are called "the law of conservation of energy". Kemble identifies it as the statement which asserts the constancy of the mean value of the Hamiltonian function in time, $d\overline{H}/dt = 0$.[136] Landau and Lifshitz, Dirac, and Merzbacher identify it as the statement which asserts the constancy of the energy in time, $dE/dt = 0$.[137] Still others straddle the fence. They derive $d\overline{H}/dt = 0$ and call it "the quantum mechanical analogue" of the law; [138] "the conservation of the mean energy"; [139] and the conservation of energy "in terms of expectation values". [140] Still others call the energy a constant of motion as a result of the derivation of $d\overline{H}/dt = 0$ but not a conserved quantity. [141]

It is not terribly important which equation one calls "the law of conservation of energy" so long as none of the facts are overlooked (though it seems misleading to call $d\overline{H}/dt = 0$ the law, because it is about mean values instead of the energy of individual systems). The facts are: (i) $d\overline{H}/dt = 0$ has the same generality as the classical law and is indirectly about the energy of individual systems, though it is about the mean value of the energy. (In this paragraph I intend to use the word "energy" without prejudging the issue of meaning or reference. At this point in the argument, the reader may understand "energy" in the way Feyerabend claims it is to be understood. I shall argue

133 Feyerabend, " 'Meaning' ", pp. 180-81. He does two things in this passage. He argues for the meaning change of "energy" in the classical-quantum theoretical transition; and he is attacking Achinstein's argument that since certain principles are retained in successor theories, the terms involved must have some common meaning.
134 **Ibid.**, p. 181.
135 **Ibid.**
136 Edwin C. Kemble, **The Fundamental Principles of Quantum Mechanics** (New York: Dover, 1958), p. 288.
137 Landau and Lifshitz, **Quantum Mechanics**, pp. 27, 28; Dirac, **Quantum Mechanics**, p. 115; Merzbacher, **Quantum Mechanics**, p. 147.
138 Tolman, **Statistical Mechanics**, p. 241.
139 Bohm, **Quantum Theory**, p. 198.
140 Merzbacher, **Quantum Mechanics**, p. 43.
141 Messiah, **Quantum Mechanics**, Vol. 1, pp. 195, 211. Goldstein shows that to call the Hamiltonian a constant of motion and to call it the total energy are separate matters, for when the generalized coordinates involve the time explicitly and the Hamiltonian does not, the Hamiltonian is a constant of motion but is not the total energy. See: **Classical Mechanics**, p. 221.

against that claim later). (ii) $dE/dt = 0$ is not about the mean value of the energy but is about the energy of individual systems, though it does not have the generality of the classical laws (because it holds only for stationary states or states represented by an energy eigenfunction); and finally (iii) if the classical second law is derivable from quantum mechanics (and I have argued that it is), the familiar conservation law is derivable from it as the first integral.

Whichever statement is identified as the law, it is clear that the statement itself does not contain Hermitian operators as Feyerabend claims. True, the operators are used to derive the statements in quantum theory, but the statements themselves do not contain them. And the fact that the **sentences** "$d\bar{H}/dt = 0$" and "$dE/dt = 0$" are derived in different ways in quantum and classical theory does not entail that the meaning of the sentences and therefore of the constituent terms is different. To so argue would be to make the mistake that "**p**" means something different in "**p & q**, so **p**" and "**p & r**, so **p**"; one could not then have two proofs of the same sentence with the same meaning. [142]

So much for Feyerabend's first ground.

(b) "[The conservation laws of quantum theory] allow for 'virtual states' which are, strictly speaking, incompatible with conservation. No such states are possible in classical physics." [143]

This argument is incomprehensible. If virtual states are, "strictly speaking, incompatible with conservation", then such states are not allowed by quantum theory either and no difference has been shown between the laws as they occur in quantum theory and those laws as they occur in classical mechanics. On the other hand, if virtual states or particles are allowed — i.e., the assumption of their existence as **real** states is compatible with the conservation laws — then Feyerabend has a case for saying, "the conservation laws of quantum theory share only the name with the corresponding laws of classical physics". But this is not what is assumed. The very point of characterizing them as virtual is to flag their non-reality.

Let me give some background here.

According to the uncertainty principle, the product of the

---

142 This mistake is not without precedent: "Es kann nicht zwei unabhängige Beweise eines mathematischen Satzes geben", (Ludwig Wittgenstein, **Philosophische Bemerkungen** [Oxford: Basil Blackwell, 1964], p. 184.) This juxtaposition is not accidental since Feyerabend sees Wittgenstein as giving a "special" contextual theory of meaning and himself as giving a "general" theory (see: Feyerabend, "Explanation, Reduction", pp. 68, particularly footnote 83.)

143 Feyerabend, " 'Meaning' ", p. 181.

uncertainty of the energy and the uncertainty of the duration of the process is equal to $\hbar$, that is, Planck's constant over 2π; i.e. $\Delta E \Delta t = \hbar$. This means that $\Delta t = \hbar / \Delta E$. So if a process, say, the breakup of a proton into a neutron and positive pion, requires more energy to occur than is initially available to it, say, 140 million electron volts (140 Mev), then such a process could occur if it occurred within 5×10^{-24} sec. (since $\hbar = 7 \times 10^{-22}$ Mev.-sec.) Then as far as the uncertainty principle is concerned, the breakup could occur. [144] However, the breakup violates conservation of energy. Because of this, and because the intermediate state is not observable, the state is not considered to be a real state:

> The introduction of intermediate states is an auxiliary computational method. These states are not realised in actual fact; this is, in particular, clear from the fact that when the system goes into the intermediate state, the energy conservation law is not satisfied. [145]

On the other hand, things look **as if** the states were real, so one cannot be content with saying that the states do not exist — period. [146] For these reasons the states are called "virtual states".

So, ontologically, virtual states are like the virtual images of geometrical optics. [147] Just as treating the virtual image behind a mirror as if it is real accounts for the appearances, so treating the virtual intermediate states as if they are real accounts for the appearances. But while it is not on grounds of principle but of observation that virtual images are virtual (a piece of paper behind the mirror will not reveal the image that we see in the mirror), it is on grounds of both principle and observation that the virtual states are virtual, namely, their violation of the conservation law if they are considered real and their direct unobservability.

Some use another idea to describe virtual processes: "From the vacuum a photon with low energy may **borrow**, for an instant, energy sufficient to create one or more electron-positron pairs". [148] Here the Dirac Hole Theory is used, where one has an infinite sea of electrons in negative energy states in the electron vacuum state. The energy is borrowed from this sea. The result is the phenomenon called

---

144 The example comes from Ford, **Elementary Particles**, p. 171.

145 A.S. Davydov, **Quantum Mechanics** (Reading, Mass.: Addison-Wesley, 1965), pp. 323, 648. Also see: Julian Schwinger, **Particles, Sources, and Fields** (Reading, Mass.: Addison-Wesley, 1970), p. 267.

146 R. Hofstadter, "Structure of Nuclei and Nucleons", **Science** 136 (1962) 1013-22.

147 Another good analogy is the quasi-particles of superfluid theory: F. Reif, "Superfluidity and 'Quasi-Particles' ", **Scientific American** 203 (November, 1960) 138-50.

148 J. Kuasnica, **Physical Fields** (London: Iliffe Books, 1964), p. 177, underline is mine.

the polarization of the vacuum. [149] The point is that it is clear how energy is conserved under this picture, so the virtual state is not incompatible with it. If one takes the Hole theory seriously, there does not seem to be anything virtual about the virtual state, in which case one also has a situation which is compatible with the classical conservation law. No difference with the classical case has been demonstrated. If one does not take the Hole theory seriously, then it is also clear that conservation of energy does not allow such a state to be real.

So much for Feyerabend's second ground.

(c) "[The conservation laws of quantum theory] make use of properties that cannot be universalised simultaneously (position in the potential energy, momentum in the kinetic part) whereas classical properties can always be universalized." [150]

Feyerabend also uses this as a direct argument for incommensurability.

It will not do for either purpose. Two cases of properties which were thought to be universalizable at one time and were discovered later to be non-universalizable will show this (one case is imaginary). I give two cases, one which is scientific, one which is not, so that the complaint cannot be made that my case is either too much like the case at hand or too unlike it.

(i) One may imagine the following situation (something like it may be true for all I know): we believe that every human being is either male or female and none both. One day it is discovered that there is a human being who is not only hermaphroditic but who also has some cells with one x chromosome (male determinant) and some with two (female determinant). Here we have discovered empirically that the exclusive disjunctive property does not apply universally. Clearly no change of meaning has occurred; "male", "female", and "sex" still mean the same. One could describe this in another way which does not suggest (misleadingly) that meaning has changed: It was discovered that not every human being is male or female and none both.

(ii) During the early twenties of this century and for some time before, it was believed that the concept of charge applied to every elementary particle. [151] But with that view it was impossible to explain both the mass and the electrical neutrality of even simple atoms like those of helium, let alone more complex atoms like those of nitrogen. As is well known, in 1932 Chadwick established the existence of an electrically neutral

149 J.J. Sakurai, **Advanced Quantum Mechanics** (Reading, Mass · Addison-Wesley, 1967), pp. 138-40.
150 Feyerabend, " 'Meaning' ", p. 181.
151 Henry A. Boorse and Lloyd Motz, **The World of the Atom**, Vol. 2 (New York: Basic Books, 1965), p. 1289.

elementary particle with a mass roughly equal to that of a proton. This particle, the neutron, explained the mass and the electrical neutrality of the simple atoms. By this discovery Chadwick also showed that the concept of charge does not apply to every elementary particle. His discovery was the result of both experiment (his experiments with beryllium, boron, and nitrogen) and theory (quantum theory plus the conservation of energy and momentum). Still no one would say "charge" changed meaning as a result of all of this.

Similarly for the limitations on the "universalizability" of the concepts of position and momentum and the other conjugate dynamical variables (under the standard interpretation of the uncertainty relations). These limitations were seen to be the result of both experiment (the experiments behind the laws of optics and the de Broglie relations) and theory (quantum theory). [152] To put it in the material mode: it was discovered that an electron (or any elementary particle) does not always have a determinate position or momentum. Nothing follows about the meaning of "position", "momentum", or any function of the position or momentum; in particular nothing follows about the meaning of "kinetic energy" or "potential energy". **A fortiori** it does not follow "that the 'conservation laws' of quantum theory share only the name with the corresponding laws of classical physics".

Moreover, that conclusion is false. In quantum theory, kinetic energy is still the energy of a body or system of bodies due to the motion of the body or bodies, and potential energy is still the energy of a body or system of bodies due to the position of the body or system of bodies. And total energy which is represented by the Hamiltonian is still the sum of those two (subject to the caveat of footnote 141). All this in spite of the fact that these dynamical quantities are represented in a different way part of the time (namely by operators). This is shown by the fact that in every major presentation of quantum theory the operators are introduced as being associated with the dynamical properties and it is understood what dynamical properties are being talked about, namely, those mentioned above, the same ones of which the classical authors wrote. No indication is given that the referent of the expressions "E", "T", and "V", etc. have been changed. If the referent had been changed, it would have been indicated in some way. Moreover, a case similar to that made for mass in section 5.6 can be made here for "E", "T", and "V". So the reference has been stable. More important, there **is** something common to the

152 Werner Heisenberg, **The Physical Principles of the Quantum Theory** (New York: Dover, 1930), pp. 14, 15.

law of conservation of energy in both theories — they are about the energy — if you like, the same energy. And this result is sufficient to show that the first integral of the classical second law which is derivable from quantum theory **is** the familiar conservation of energy theorem.

5.9 Summary

I have defended the deductivist thesis against all the criticisms raised in the literature. I have seen no criticisms of the alleged deductive relations obtaining between wave optics and geometrical optics or between the general theory of relativity and the special theory. [153] These cases raise no new problems which are peculiar to them nor do they raise any new problems of principle. Thus I have not discussed them. If anyone wishes to take issue with these cases, I shall have to deal with them later and in another place.

While I have not constructed the familiar derivations which are accessible enough in the standard texts, I have indicated how they go. The disagreement concerning them has arisen over the identity of the conclusions of the derivation rather than with the mathematical detail. Thus in each case I have argued for the identity of the conclusion as being the relevant statement of the less comprehensive theory rather than some stand-in. Thus I have shown in each case that the less comprehensive is derivable from the more comprehensive theory.

6. Ground Clearing for Conclusions

In earlier discussions the relations between Galileo's law and Newtonian gravitational theory, classical thermodynamics and statistical mechanics, physical optics and electromagnetic theory, and so on have all been discussed under the head of reduction. That this is a mistake can be seen from the following considerations: [154] Newton's gravitational theory reduces to Galileo's law (under certain conditions) and quantum theory reduces to classical mechanics (under certain conditions). In these cases it is the more comprehensive theory that reduces to the less comprehensive theory. On the other hand, classical thermodynamics is (has been) reduced to statistical mechanics, and physical optics is (has been) reduced to electromagnetic theory. Here the less comprehensive theory is reduced to the more comprehensive. What is reduced to what, plus the slight difference in the locutions one feels comfortable with, shows that we are in fact dealing with two relations and not one. This is further confirmed when it is seen that while thermodynamics

153 Deductions as they occur in Born and Wolf, **Optics**, p. 109-21; or Luneberg, **Mathematical Theory**, pp. 1-25; and Tolman, **Relativity**, pp. 185-87; or Misner, Thorne, and Wheeler, **Gravitation**, pp. 143.
154 This was also argued by Nickles in "Two Concepts", pp. 181-201.

has been reduced to statistical mechanics, quantum theory **has not been reduced** to classical mechanics. And while quantum theory **reduces** to classical mechanics (under certain circumstances), it is **not** the case that thermodynamics **reduces** to statistical mechanics (under certain circumstances).

There are other differences. It makes sense to say "Thermodynamics was reduced to statistical mechanics in 1904" to describe the present relation between the theories. It does not make any sense to say "Quantum theory was reduced to classical mechanics in 1904" to describe the present relation between the theories.

When we say that quantum theory reduces to classical mechanics we mean that quantum theory can be transformed into (can be shown to be identical with) classical mechanics under certain conditions. It is not a consequence of this claim that one's ontology contains less than one might have thought, for it is an antecedent condition for this relation to obtain that the subject matter of the principles of the less comprehensive theory be a subset of the subject matter of the principles of the more comprehensive theory. To ask: "Does theory **T** reduce to theory **T'**?" is to presuppose that the subject matter of the principles of theory **T'** is a subset of the subject matter of the principles of **T**. This relation has no generally accepted name which distinguishes it from the other relation. I shall call it "theoretical transformation".

When we say thermodynamics has been reduced to statistical mechanics, we mean that thermodynamics has been shown to be nothing more than a part of (a branch of) statistical mechanics, i.e. that the subject matter of thermodynamics is not different from that of statistical mechanics. So to show that the less comprehensive theory has been reduced to the more comprehensive theory is to show that the subject matter of the principles of the less comprehensive theory is a subset of the subject matter of the principles of the more comprehensive theory. Consequently to ask: "Can theory **T'** be reduced to theory **T** ?" is to ask if the subject matter of the principles of **T'** is a subset of the subject matter of the principles of **T**; it is not to presuppose it. This relation **is** properly discussed under the head of reduction, as it involves the diminishing of the apparent ontology.

I shall call the class of which both these relations are members "intertheoretical relations", which name has some acceptance.

There is a third kind of intertheoretical relation, which differs strikingly from those that have been discussed. I have in mind here the relation which obtains between the early phlogiston theories of reduction, calcination, and respiration, and those of

Lavoisier. It has been taken as obvious that there is no deductive connection between these theories. And this "fact" has always been held as an ace up the sleeve of the non-deductivists. The caloric and kinetic theories of heat have been used in the same fashion. So it will be worthwhile looking at these theories, both to give examples of the third kind of relation and to show that the aces can be beat.

The early phlogiston theory could account for most of the chemical phenomena known in the mid-eighteenth century. [155] For example the reduction of an ore was explained as being accomplished by the metallic ore taking up phlogiston (ϕ) from charcoal upon heating. In modern unbalanced notation:

A. metallic ore $+ \phi +$ charcoal $\xrightarrow{heat}$ metal

According to the theory of reduction of Lavoisier, when the metallic ore is heated in the presence of charcoal it gives up oxygen, thereby releasing the metal:

B. metallic ore $+$ charcoal $\xrightarrow{heat}$ metal $+ O_2$

Now **A** is derivable from **B** via the identity which says that phlogiston is negative oxygen: [156]

C. $\phi = -O_2$

This identity is not the ordinary theoretical identity by any means. The identity does not presuppose or entail the existence of phlogiston. Indeed it implies its non-existence as it is usually understood. This identity statement is best translated as: "There is nothing more to ϕ than $-O_2$". [157] It is a summary way of claiming the following: those processes which the early phlogiston theory claimed involved phlogiston as a reactant in fact involved oxygen as a product; and those processes which the theory claimed involved phlogiston as a product in fact involved oxygen as a reactant. The translation of the identity into "There is nothing more to ϕ than $-O_2$" brings out the fact that this identity is not symmetrical: "There is nothing more to phlogiston than negative oxygen" does not entail "There is nothing more to negative oxygen than phlogiston". (One might think of the pair: "There is nothing more to satanic possession than self-hypnosis" and "There is nothing more to self-hypnosis than satanic possession".) Further, the identity is

155 James Bryant Conant, "The Overthrow of the Phlogiston Theory: The Chemical Revolution of 1775-1789", in **Harvard Case Histories in Experimental Science**, Vol. 1, ed. James Bryant Conant and Leonard K. Nash (Cambridge: Harvard University Press, 1957), p.70.

156 Kopp, **Geschichte der Chemie** (Brunswick, 1843), pp. 150 f. cited in J.R. Partington and Douglas McKie, "Historical Studies on the Phlogiston Theory - I. The Levity of Phlogiston", **Annals of Science** 2 (October 15, 1937) p. 361. While this characterization may be part of an oversimplified history as Partington claims, this does not count against this identification for one stage of the history of the theory.

157 This translation is suggested by some work (which so far as I know has no title) of Terry Penner's.

not reflexive because if it makes any sense at all, it is false that there is nothing more to phlogiston than phlogiston.

One can easily see how the derivation goes. By "subtracting" O_2 from both sides of **B** one gets

metallic ore + charcoal $-O_2$ $\overset{heat}{\rightarrow}$ metal

Then using **C**,

metallic ore + charcoal + ϕ $\overset{heat}{\rightarrow}$ metal

Which is **A**. Clearly, the phlogiston theory of reduction is derivable from that of Lavoisier. One can construct similar derivations for the later phlogiston theory, in which phlogiston (often carrying water) is hydrogen. [158]

I shall call the relation which obtains between these two theories "explimination" because it involves the **expl**anation of an el**imination** of a theoretical entity. Like theoretical transformations and reductions, explimination is used to explain the successes and failures of the less comprehensive theory. Unlike those theories it is the basis for an elimination of an item from our ontology, in particular the elimination of an element of the subject matter of the principles of the less comprehensive theory. The connection between these two is that the explanation of the successes of the less comprehensive theory shows that the entity to be eliminated can be eliminated by showing that its existence is not necessary to account for the phenomena which the less comprehensive theory has explained. Explanation of the failures of the less comprehensive theory give additional reason for believing that there is no such entity as that postulated. In the case of the phlogiston theory it was because the metallic ore gave something off, namely, oxygen, that the metal weighed less than the ore. The mere fact that the theory of Lavoisier accounts for some facts which the phlogiston theory does not counts against the existence of phlogiston.

Like reduction and unlike theoretical transformation, explimination involves an essential use of an identity. The identity is the means by which one derives the statements which ostensibly refer to the entity which has been eliminated. One thereby accounts for the success of the less comprehensive theory. Unlike reduction, the identity is not a full blown theoretical identity. Though it may appear in the same guise, "$x = y$", it is best translated as "There is nothing more to x than y". I shall call such identities expliminative identities. Expliminative identity statements imply the non-existence of the entity ostensibly referred to by the first term of the identity statements, as that term is usually understood. An expliminative identity statement of the form "$x = y$" implies

158 Conant, "Phlogiston Theory", p. 110.

that there are no x's as "x" is usually conceived. This is brought out by the translation "There is nothing more to x than y". This feature makes the expliminative identity relation nonsymmetrical, for one is not committed to the existence or nonexistence of y in asserting this identity. Both are possible. For example, in asserting "Demonic possession is self-hypnosis" one would want to say that the y (self-hypnosis) exists; in asserting "An infinitesimal is a ghost of a departed quantity" Berkeley did not want to say that the y (ghosts of departed quantities) exists. Consequently when the y exists and one turns the relata around the relation, one will get a false statement. "Demonic possession is self-hypnosis" could be true while "Self-hypnosis is demonic possession" is false. To see this most clearly, one should consider the translations of these two statements again.

I shall illustrate the explimination relation as it obtains in the case of the caloric and kinetic theories of heat. In so doing I shall show that the commonly held view that the first is not derivable from the second is false. The caloric theory of heat, at least the developed part, is derivable from the kinetic theory. Its most developed form can be found in Carnot's **Reflections on the Motive Power of Fire** and in Émile Clapeyron's **Memoir on the Motive Power of Heat**. [159] (Clapeyron expressed the ideas of Carnot in analytic form.) The fundamental assumptions of Carnot's caloric theory are: A_1 that heat is a material substance composed of fine particles, and A_2 that "...the equivalent of the work done by heat is found in the mere transfer of heat from a hotter to a colder body, while the quantity of heat [caloric] remains undiminished". [160]

This theoretical point of view was developed by Carnot and Clapeyron for so-called "permanent" gases, that is, gases which are difficult to liquefy, and which were therefore thought to be non-liquefiable. For such gases in a chamber with a movable wall the second principle, A_2, leads to the equation

   B. $dQ/dV = RC/V$

where Q is the amount of heat [caloric] transferred from the hotter to the cooler body, in this case, the amount of heat absorbed by the gas; V is the volume of the gas; R is the gas constant and C is an unknown function of the temperature. [161]

159 Both of which, as well as Clausius' work **On the Motive Power of Heat, and on the Laws which can be Deduced from it for the Theory of Heat**, can be found in Sadi Carnot, **Reflections on the Motive Power of Fire**, ed. E. Mendoza (New York: Dover, 1960).

160 Clausius, **Motive Power**, p. 132. I use the Clausius' formulation because he breaks the principle into two parts. (The reason for the desirability of this shall become evident below.) Carnot said: "The production of motive power is then due in steam-engines not to an actual consumption of caloric, but **to its transportation from a warm body to a cold body**....We shall see shortly that this principle is applicable to any machine set in motion by heat." (**Reflections**, p. 7.)

161 Clapeyron, **Memoir**, p. 102.

This is one of two "analytical expressions of Carnot's principle, as they are given by Clapeyron". [162]

Now **B** can be derived in the following way: from the kinetic theory one can derive the gas law:

(i) $PV = RT$

where P is the gas pressure. [163] And from statistical mechanics one can derive the first law of thermodynamics, $\Delta U = JQ -W$ [164], where U is the internal energy, Q is the heat added to the system, J is the mechanical equivalent of heat, and W is the work done on the system. For a gas in a piston this becomes

(ii) $dU = JdQ_c - PdV$

where Q_c is the heat added in a specific change. [165] Now one assumes the expliminative identity statement, which says that there is nothing more to caloric than molecular motion and can be put

(iii) $dQ = dQ_c$.

Assume further, as is approximately true, that when a permanent gas is expanded isothermally it absorbs only as much heat as is used in the transition, in other words assume that the differential change in internal energy is zero, i.e.

(iv) $dU = 0$. [166]

Finally, assume that

(v) $C = T/J$

where C is the "unknown" function of temperature. Then from (ii), (iii), and (iv) one gets

$JdQ - PdV = 0$

or

(vi) $dQ = PdV/J$

By rearranging (i) we get

(vii) $P = RT/V$

Then substituting (vii) in (vi),

$dQ = (RT/VJ)dV$

which upon rearranging becomes

$dQ/dV = RT/VJ$

and substituting (v) in this one gets

(viii) $dQ/dV = RC/V$

which is the analytical expression of Carnot's principle **B**.

The only additional assumptions that have been made are (iii), (iv), and (v). Assumption (iii) is simply the expliminative identity. Assumption (iv) is an assumption that can be, and is,

162 Clausius, **Motive Power**, p. 136.
163 For example, Arnold Sommerfield, **Lectures on Theoretical Physics**, Vol. 5: **Thermodynamics and Statistical Mechanics** (New York: Academic, 1964), pp. 169-72.
164 For example, Tolman, **Statistical Mechanics**, pp. 528-30.
165 See Franzo H. Crawford, **Heat, Thermodynamics, and Statistical Physics** (New York: Harcourt, Brace & World, 1963), pp. 103, 111.
166 Clausius, **Motive Power**, p. 128.

made independent of the kinetic or caloric theories, and is approximately true. Assumption (v) is made on empirical grounds. [167]

One qualification must be placed on this derivation. Carnot assumed (see A_2) that "...the quantity of heat remains undiminished". The derivation works only if one drops this part of the assumption:

> The latter part of this assumption—namely, that the quantity of heat remains undiminished—contradicts our former principle, and must therefore be rejected if we are to retain that principle. On the other hand, the first part may obtain in all its essentials. [168]

The assumption that the quantity of heat is conserved, though essential to **Carnot's** caloric theory (without it, the theory would not be Carnot's), is not essential to the caloric theory of heat. What is essential there is the proposition that heat is a material substance. To be sure, it was believed that the elementary particles constituting matter were indestructible, so particles of caloric were indestructible, and hence their numbers conserved. But we now know that elementary particles are destructible, for example in electron-positron annihilation, so there was neither a logical nor a physical barrier to the assumption of non-conservation of caloric. That is, the caloric theory could have used the assumption that caloric is not conserved and still have been the caloric theory.

The derivation shows that the success of the caloric theory can be explained. One of the more striking failures of the caloric theory was its inability to account for the apparent constancy of the value of the conversion factor **J** regardless of how the work was performed. [169] One might say that the first shows that the caloric theory is not necessary to explain the phenomena, while the latter shows that the caloric theory is not sufficient — caloric has been expliminated.

There are, then, at least three different intertheoretical relations: theoretical transformation, reduction, and explimination.

7. Auxiliary Assumptions

I have argued that there is a deduction in intertheoretical relations and so in reductions, expliminations and theoretical transformations, namely, when one derives the less from the more comprehensive theory in conjunction with auxiliary assumptions. But as Sklar has pointed out, to so argue would be

---

167 **Ibid.**, pp. 137-38.
168 **Ibid.**, p. 132.
169 E. Mendoza, "A Sketch for a History of Early Thermodynamics", **Physics Today** 14 (February, 1961) 38-39.

relatively useless without some specification of the allowable auxiliary assumptions

> for such an auxiliary statement . . . is all too easy to come by, unless severe restrictions are put on its nature. Just take, for example, the conditional formed of a reducing theory as antecedent and reduced theory as consequent. Such a bridging law would allow us to reduce any theory to any other. [170]

The point is well taken.

The example used to make the point shows that one restriction that is understood for auxiliary assumptions is:

(1) An auxiliary assumption is a statement that is required to derive the less comprehensive from the more comprehensive theory.

This eliminates Sklar's example because the conditional or any of its equivalents **says** what the derivation is supposed to show, namely, that the less comprehensive theory is derivable from the more comprehensive. Consequently, if it is required, it is not required. And this is just to say that it is not required and therefore is not an auxiliary assumption.

Another example which might occur (only to a philosopher) is where the auxiliary assumption is the less comprehensive theory itself. Then the less comprehensive follows from the more comprehensive plus the auxiliary assumption by simplification. This case is eliminated by the fact that this putative auxiliary assumption is not required to derive the less **from the more comprehensive theory** because the less comprehensive would follow from the auxiliary assumption alone by repetition. [171]

A second restriction emerges from the consideration of the examples:

(2) An auxiliary assumption must be true, or if false, must be approximately true though strictly speaking false; and in a successful reduction or theoretical transformation if the more comprehensive theory is true, the validity of the approximately true assumption must be identical with that of the less comprehensive theory.

By "validity" here, I mean "where the statement in question holds", and by "holds" I mean "where it is true or where it behaves as if it were true". Hence two statements with

170 Lawrence Sklar, "The Evolution of the Problem of the Unity of Science", in **Philosophical Foundations of Science** ed. R.J. Seeger and R.S. Cohen (Dordrecht: D. Reidel, 1974), pp. 540-41.

171 In this use of "derive", which occurs in common speech, but not in formal logic, if **p** can be derived from **q** alone, it is not derived **from q** & **r** where **r** is superfluous. To put the requirement in the logician's sense of "derive": An auxiliary assumption is a statement which is required to derive the less comprehensive from the more comprehensive theory, it being understood that the less comprehensive theory does not follow from the auxiliary assumption(s) alone.

identical validity behave as if they are true in the same places and times.

One purpose of exhibiting the intertheoretical relations is to explain the empirical success of the less comprehensive theory. Thus if the auxiliary assumptions are true, they must show where the less comprehensive theory is valid and where not. So the assumption that the height of certain macroscopic objects above the surface of the earth is negligible relative to the radius of the earth, shows when Galileo's law for freely falling objects is valid and when not. All of the negligibility assumptions (see section 4) are of this type. The explanatory function also implies that the validity of the approximately true auxiliary assumptions must match that of the less comprehensive theory. If assumptions have greater validity than the less comprehensive theory, the derivation (and the assumed truth of the more comprehensive theory) will imply that the less comprehensive theory is more successful than it is in fact. When no better (validity matching) auxiliary assumptions are available, one has reason for believing that the more comprehensive theory is false. If the auxiliary assumptions have less validity than the less comprehensive theory, the derivation (and the assumed truth of the more comprehensive theory) will imply that the less comprehensive theory is less successful than it is. Again, if no better (validity matching) assumptions are available, one will thereby have good reason for believing the more comprehensive theory is false. So the validity of the assumptions and the less comprehensive theory must match. The contrary to fact assumptions of section 4 — e.g. that $\hbar = 0$ — are examples of this kind. When there is a match, and assuming the less comprehensive theory has some validity, one has confirmation of the more comprehensive theory. [172]

When I speak of the auxiliary assumptions being approximately true or having a certain restricted validity, I do not mean that the statements assumed **express** this approximate character or restricted validity, for in that event the states in question might be exactly true, or true — period. For example statements like ''Planck's constant is approximately equal to zero, i.e. $h \simeq 0$'' are not approximately true, they are true — period. However, ''Planck's constant is equal to zero, i.e., $h = 0$'' is approximately true. It does not express its approximate nature, it has it. What I mean is that the proximity to the truth is a character of the statement. A glance at the

172 See for example Tolman, **Relativity**, p. 201, where having derived classical celestial mechanics from general relativity he writes: ''We can now regard all the well-tested results of celestial mechanics as furnishing important support for the relativistic theory of gravitation''. Also see: Ronald Adler, Maurice Bazin, and Menahem Schiffer, **Introduction to General Relativity** (New York: McGraw-Hill, 1965), p. 277.

intertheoretical relations in section 5, as well as any of the relevant literature, will show that it is the latter and not the former device that is used. One reason for doing it this way is that one will not obtain the law in question if one uses the strictly true statement which expresses the approximation. Another reason is that there is no simple calculus of approximations. One problem is that "approximately equals" or "approximately the same as" are not transitive relations: John may be approximately the same height as Mary, who is approximately the same height as Don, without John being approximately the same height as Don. Another problem is that the relations are not clearly symmetrical. It seems that the length of this string may be approximately equal to that of the standard meter in Paris, but the length of the standard meter in Paris is not approximately equal to that of this string. The compositional talents of my friend may be approximately equal to those of Beethoven, but the compositional talents of Beethoven are not approximately equal to those of my friend. Finally the relations are not reflexive: nothing is approximately equal to itself in any respect.

The reader will recall that in section 1, I argued that an auxiliary assumption may and often does contradict some statement of the more comprehensive theory. This requires more extended comment which will lead to a third constraint on auxiliary assumptions.

First, as I noted in section 1, in event of the incompatibility of an auxiliary assumption with a statement of the more comprehensive theory, use must not be made of the incompatibility in the derivation — otherwise the derivation would be trivial and uninformative. This implies that if the auxiliary assumption is permissible, use must not be made of the contrary or contradictory of the auxiliary assumption in the derivation.

Second, as I pointed out in section 1, it is clear that there is little sense in saying one derived one theory from another if one did not use the essential statements of the more comprehensive theory. I cannot be said to have derived Newtonian mechanics from classical statistical mechanics even though Newtonian mechanics deductively follows from classical statistical mechanics. (It follows trivially because it is the underlying mechanical theory for the statistical assumptions.) Such a deduction would not be a derivation from **statistical mechanics** because no statistical assumptions would be required for the deduction. One might as well say one derived Newtonian mechanics from itself.

From these two comments follows a third constraint on auxiliary assumptions:

(3) An auxiliary assumption may be logically incompatible

with a non-essential statement of the more comprehensive theory but it cannot be incompatible with an essential statement of the more comprehensive theory. And if the auxiliary assumption is incompatible with a non-essential statement, one cannot use the non-essential statement in the derivation. By "essential statement" I mean a statement which is essential to the theory, one without which the theory would not be the theory it is. For example, the principle of restricted relativity ("If, relative to K, K' is a uniformly moving co-ordinate system devoid of rotation, then natural phenomena run their course with respect to K' according to exactly the same general laws as with respect to K." [173]) is essential to the special theory of relativity. Without that principle one could hardly call the remaining body of statements the special theory of relativity. By contrast, Newton's laws of motion are not essential to statistical mechanics; one can use the quantum laws and still have statistical mechanics.

So much for the constraints on auxiliary assumptions. I do not know that this list is exhaustive and would not know how to go about proving it if it were. However, this list is sufficient to deal with the familiar troublesome cases — that is the best I can do here.

8. Reduction, Explimination and Theoretical Transformation

Reductions, expliminations, and theoretical transformations are species of intertheoretical relations. All serve to explain the success or lack of success of the less comprehensive theory. All involve the deduction of the less comprehensive from the more comprehensive theory in conjunction with certain auxiliary assumptions.

Schematically,

$P_1, P_2,...P_j$ } principles and postulates of the more comprehensive theory, **T**

$A_1, A_2,...A_k$ } auxiliary assumptions

$P_1', P_2'...P_l'$ } principles and postulates of the less comprehensive theory, **T'**

By "principles" of a theory I mean the basic or fundamental principles, laws, equations, hypotheses or postulates of the theory, for example, the principle of relativity, Newton's laws of motion, Maxwell's equations, the quantum hypothesis, and Bohr's quantum postulates. These "principles" **are** the theory of which they are principles, they are the source of the identity of the theory. Other statements which may be required as axioms or postulates in an axiomatic version of the theory are not essential to the theory in the sense that they may be

173 Einstein, **Relativity**, p. 13.

replaced or modified without changing the identity of the theory. Something of their **kind** may be essential, but not a particular instance of the kind. A postulate about the structure of atoms is necessary or essential for the kinetic theory, but not the particular statement that an atom has non-zero dimensionality. One could change the postulate to ''Atoms are dimensionless'' without changing the kinetic theory into another theory. A postulate about the mechanics governing the members of a statistical ensemble is essential to statistical mechanics, but not the assumption that the elements obey classical mechanics. One could change the postulate to ''The elements of a statistical ensemble obey the laws of quantum mechanics'' and still have statistical mechanics. By contrast, one cannot change the principle that the molecules of all bodies at temperatures above absolute zero are in continual motion, and still have the kinetic theory.

As we have just seen the auxiliary assumptions are subject to the following constraints:

(1) The A_i must be required to derive **T'** from **T**.
(2) The A_i must be true, or if false, must be approximately true though strictly speaking false; and if the more comprehensive theory is true, the validity of the approximately true A_i must be identical to that of **T'**.
(3) An A_i **may** be logically incompatible with a **non**essential statement of **T**, and if it is, one cannot use the nonessential statement in the derivation. An A_i cannot be logically incompatible with an essential statement of **T**.

In reduction, explimination, and theoretical transformation, the success (and failure) of **T'** confirms **T**. Constraint (2) leaves us with two possibilities: either the A_i are true, or they are approximately true (though strictly speaking false). When the A_i are true and **T'** is derivable from **T**, the success of **T'** confirms **T**, and this is so because the failure of **T'** would disconfirm **T**. When the A_i are approximately true and **T'** is derivable from **T**, by constraint (2) the validity of **T'** must match that of the A_i. If it does not and no ''better'' A_i (i.e. A_i which inconjunction with **T** entail **T'** with a validity to match **T'**) are available, then **T** must be false. So if the validity matches, **T** is confirmed, that is, the success as well as the failure of **T'** confirms **T**.

Now ''**T** reduces to **T'** under certain circumstances'', ''**T'** can be reduced to **T''**'' and ''**T** expliminates **T'''**'' are verified in the same way, namely, by deriving **T'** from the conjunction of **T** and the A_i. So the difference between them does not reside in the mere fact of the deduction. I claim that the differences between the various intertheoretical relations is to be made out on the basis of the purposes served by the deductions.

Deductions can serve many purposes. One purpose which looms very large in other contexts is to establish the truth of that which is derived. This is not usually the purpose of the deductions with which we are concerned. Indeed it is often the other way around: one point of derivation is to show that the known truth or approximate truth of what is derived is evidence for that from which it is derived, as we have just seen. Another use of a derivation is simply to show that a certain sentence is a theorem in a certain formal system. This is not usually the purpose of the derivations that are our present concern either. The languages are not formal and one is not concerned solely to show relations between various sets of sentences.

The purpose of the deduction in theoretical transformation is to show that under certain conditions part of **T** becomes identical with **T'**. It is an answer to the question "Can **T** be reduced to **T'**?", which means "Can **T** be transformed into **T'** under certain conditions?" It is understood at the outset that the subject matters of the principles and postulates are not distinct. Unless this were understood the question "Can **T** be transformed into **T'** under certain circumstances?" would make little sense. In short:

> To **theoretically transform T** into **T'** is to deduce **T'** from the conjunction of **T** and the A_i in order to show that under certain conditions expressed by the A_i, **T** becomes identical with **T'**. No theoretical identity need occur amongst the A_i because the subject matter of the principles and postulates of **T'** is a subset of that of **T**.

So we have seen that Newtonian gravitational theory and mechanics reduces to Kepler's laws when the effects of the other bodies in the universe are ignored, and reduces to Galileo's law for freely falling bodies when the effects of the other bodies in the universe as well as the height above the surface of the earth are ignored. Special relativity reduces to classical mechanics when the velocity of light is infinite, and quantum theory reduces to classical theory when Planck's constant is negligible.

By contrast, the purpose of the deduction in reduction which distinguishes reduction from the others is to show that the set of objects, substances, properties, events or actions that form the subject matter of the principles and postulates of **T'** is a subset of the set of objects, substances, properties, events or actions that form the subject matter of the principles and postulates of **T**. It is an answer to the question "Can **T'** be reduced to **T**?", which means "Can it be shown **that** the set of objects, etc. that are the subject matter of the principles and postulates of **T'** is a subset of the set of objects, etc. that are the subject matter of the principles and postulates of **T**?" or "Can it be shown that the first set is not distinct from the second?"

So there will usually be a **prima facie** difference between the subject matter of the principles and postulates of **T'** and that of **T**. This **prima facie** difference in subject matter is often due to a disparity in vocabulary, for example, "temperature" occurs in the usual (English) statements of thermodynamics, but does not occur in the usual (English) statements of the kinetic theory of matter. But the real difference is an initial conceptual difference — that is, however we talk about the temperature, whether we use the French word "température" or the German word "temperatur", the word will initially mean something different from any word of the corresponding statement of, say, statistical mechanics. "Temperature" did not (and does not) mean "mean kinetic energy" and "light" did not (and does not) mean "electromagnetic radiation in the frequency range from approximately 4×10^{14} sec^{-1} to 7.5×10^{14} sec^{-1}". The disparity in vocabulary is relatively unimportant, for there is no logical reason for excluding the possibility that some language uses a single word ambiguously so that it means the same as "temperature" in one use, and means the same as "mean kinetic energy" in another use. In such a situation there would still be a **prima facie** difference in subject matter between the principles of thermodynamics and those of statistical mechanics. (Suppose for example, "tempergy" was used to mean the measure of the intensity of heat in thermodynamics and was used to mean the arithmetical average value of the energy due to the motion of the constituent molecules in statistical mechanics; in spite of the identity of the vocabulary it would appear that there was a difference in subject matter in the two theories just because of the conceptual [meaning] difference.) So it is the conceptual difference that is responsible for the **prima facie** difference in subject matter. [174] This is where the theoretical identity comes in. The theoretical identity claims that the subject matters of the principles and postulates which appear to be distinct are not in fact. So a non-superfluous use of the theoretical identities is necessary for a reduction. To summarize:

To **reduce T'** to **T** is to deduce **T'**, which is conceptually (meaning) distinct from **T**, from the conjunction of **T** and the A_i in order to show that the subject matter of the principles and postulates of **T'** is not distinct from that of the principles and postulates of **T**. For this purpose a theoretical identity is necessary as an A_i.

So, physical optics has been reduced to electromagnetic theory,

---

174 This is one respect in which reduction differs from Nagel's "inhomogeneous reduction". (See: Nagel, "Issues", p. 119.) Nagel's "homogeneous-inhomogeneous reduction" distinction is made on the basis of vocabulary, which makes the distinction curiously language relative.

and thermodynamics to statistical mechanics. In addition, given the reading of the impetus theory of section 5.1, we may say that the impetus theory has been reduced to the mechanics of Newton.

Finally, the purpose of the deduction in explimination is to provide a basis for eliminating an item in the subject matter of the principles of T' from our ontology. It is understood prior to the explimination — in other words it is presupposed — that the subject matter of the two sets of principles and postulates is distinct in some respect (usually in theoretical entities, for example, phlogiston is not a subject of Lavoisier's theoretical principles, caloric is not part of the subject matter of the principles or postulates of the kinetic theory). Further, it is presupposed that there is evidence for the falsity of T'. Explimination then provides the basis for the elimination by showing that T can explain the success(es) of T' as well as the failures. By showing that T can explain the success(es) of T', explimination shows that the elements of the subject matter of the principles and postulates of T' that are distinct from those of T are not required to account for the phenomena for which T' accounts. By showing that Lavoisier's theory of reduction can account for the success of the phlogiston theory, the explimination shows that phlogiston is not required to account for the reduction of a metallic ore. At the same time an explimination shows that there is nothing more to the distinct (from T) elements of the subject matter of T' than some elements of the principles of T and so justifies the elimination of those elements from our ontology. The deduction of the phlogiston theory from Lavoisier's theory shows (providing Lavoisier's theory is true) that there is nothing more to phlogiston than negative oxygen and so justifies the elimination of phlogiston from our ontology. In order to accomplish this an expliminative identity is needed to bridge the gap left by the distinct elements of the subject matter. To summarize:

> To **expliminate** T' is to deduce the defective theory T' from the conjunction of T and the A_i in order to provide a basis for eliminating an element in the subject matter of the principles or postulates of T' from our ontology — it being understood that the subject matter of the respective principles are in part distinct. For this reason an expliminative identity must occur amongst the A_i.

There is, then, a deduction in theoretical transformation, reduction and explimination, so there is a deduction in reduction in the generic (and sloppy) sense of the word "reduction". And this is what I set out to show.

One immediate consequence of this discussion is that Feyerabend's case against the deductive-nomological theory of explanation [175] vanishes, for the whole case consisted of arguing that the laws (or theory) to be explained cannot be derived from the explanans theory. So if the D-N model is to be attacked (and I am of the opinion that it should), it should not be attacked on this ground.

A second consequence of this discussion is that the paradigm-change-involves-change-of-meaning-of-"established and familiar"-terms view of Kuhn[176] is false. It will be recalled that Kuhn had a referential theory of meaning, so the claim comes down to a change-in-reference-in-change-of-paradigm view. But we have seen that the theoretical identities involved in a reduction presuppose (initially and in all known cases) retention of previous semantic commitments. Theoretical transformations presuppose retention of the referents, and explimination also retains the previous semantic commitments by denying the existence of the referent as it is usually conceived.

From the supposed change of reference Kuhn concluded, "In the passage to the limit it is not only the forms of the laws that have changed. Simultaneously we have had to alter the fundamental structural elements of which the universe to which they apply is composed." [177] The stability of reference in the intertheoretical relations considered shows that this metaphysical conclusion is false.

To conclude on a positive note, we have seen that the cumulative view of scientific change has good support (contrary to Kuhn). We have seen that the success of the superseded theory in the cases examined has been "absorbed" by the superseding theory, that is, what is right about the theory can be accounted for. So nothing worth saving is cast aside or replaced in these cases, it is "recoverable" via the appropriate auxiliary assumptions.

175 Feyerabend, "Explanation, Reduction".
176 Kuhn, **Revolutions**, p. 102.
177 **Ibid.**

APPENDIX

On the Referent of "Mass"

I shall argue in what follows that in both the special theory and Newtonian mechanics, "mass" refers to that property of a body in virtue of which it resists a change in motion; the parameter "m" refers, therefore, to the magnitude or measure of that property of a body in virtue of which it resists a change in motion.

There should be little disagreement that this is at least **part** of the reference of "mass" in Newtonian or classical mechanics. Standard introductory texts "define" "mass" in this way. (See for example, R.P. Feynman, R.B. Leighton, and M. Sands, **The Feynman Lectures on Physics** Vol. 1 [Reading, Mass: Addison-Wesley, 1963], p. 9-1; D. Halliday and R. Resnick, **Physics for Students of Science and Engineering**, Combined ed. [New York: John Wiley & Sons, 1960, 1962], p. 68; and G. Shortley and D. Williams, **Principles of College Physics** [Englewood Cliffs: Prentice-Hall, 1959], p. 52.) And Max Jammer writes:

> Now, classical, or what is usually called Newtonian mechanics takes this resistance to change of motion, different in different bodies but a constant for the same body, as the ultimate and absolute individual characteristic of the given body; "inertial mass", as this absolute parameter is called, thus becomes for a given body an irreducible magnitude, on which other parameters depend, but which itself is independent of anything else. [178]

Further, it does not even make sense to talk of mass in a world in which it is not the property in virtue of which a body resists a change in motion. That is, this is a necessary characteristic of the referent of "mass".

This raises the question of what more should be added to characterize the referent (if this is not enough). Kuhn would claim that we must add at least that it is a conserved quantity. But this will not do for reasons already discussed (in section 5.6). This additional characteristic must be a necessary characteristic or a contingent one. That it cannot be a necessary characteristic can be shown by a line of reasoning similar in form to that in section 5.6: if it referred to such a characteristic, the law of conservation of mass would be self-referring, necessary, analytic and **a priori**. It is none of these, for it is false (as we shall see), so "mass" does not refer to a property which is necessarily conserved in Newtonian mechanics. It is clear by now that it does not refer to a property that is contingently conserved either for the simple fact that the **classical descriptions** of binding energy and pair production and annihilation experiments show that the referent of "mass" in classical mechanics is not conserved. In the first case, the sum of the masses of the

178 Max Jammer, **Concepts of Mass** (New York: Harper & Row, 1961), p. 71. Two points should be noted. The phrase "different in different bodies but a constant for the same body" is either inappropriate, because in the sentence it implies a falsehood, or is a comment on "body" rather than on mass. It is quite common to speak of variable masses (even as functions of the velocity) in classical or Newtonian mechanics, for example, the mass of a load of sand in an operating street sander will vary as will that of rocket fuel in an operating rocket. This refutes many claims to the contrary (see, for example, William Ruddick, "Physical Equations and Identity", ed. Milton Munitz, **Identity and Individuation** (New York: New York University Press, 1971], p. 248). On the other hand Jammer may be speaking of Newtonian ultimate or fundamental bodies, in which case it may be true, but not a necessary characteristic of mass. Second, Newton did not define "mass" in this way. He said it was the product of the density and the volume (see **Principia**, definiton I). However Newton did say some similar sorts of things, viz. that mass is that which is responsible for resistance to change of motion (see: Jammer, **Mass**, pp. 71, 72, 81; and **Principia**, definition III). This is not a definition but could be used to fix the reference of "mass" and obviously was later. In any case Newtonian or classical mechanics is not identical with what was written in the **Principia** as Jammer also notes (**Ibid.**, p. 72).

components of a nucleus is not equal to the mass of the nucleus. In the case of pair production one has more mass after the interaction than before, and in the case of annihilation one has less mass after the interaction than before. Other possible candidates which suffer the same defects are constancy of mass of elementary particles in motion relative to an observer and a constant of proportionality in $F \propto a$ where F is the force and a is the acceleration. The falsity of both was shown by the electron mass increase with velocity experiments under classical description.

Now there are other characteristics which serve to fix the reference of "mass" in Newtonian mechanics contingently, for example, the property which Newtonian mechanics **says** (claims, asserts) is conserved and is constant for elementary particles in motion relative to the observer, and so on. But such characteristics will not help the meaning variance theorist, for they are quite compatible with anything the referential stability theorist (he who holds that the reference of a term is the same in the important theoretical transitions) would want to say about the referent of "mass" in the special theory. Indeed the only characteristics that will do for the meaning variance theorist are those that are incompatible with those he wants to attribute to the referent of "mass" in special relativity. And we have seen that none of them will serve to characterize the referent of "mass" in Newtonian mechanics.

So there are no additional characteristics of the referent of "mass" in classical mechanics which will help the meaning variance theorist.

In the more common formulation of the special theory, where "mass" seems to be used synonymously with "relativistic mass", "mass" refers **at least** to that property in virtue of which a body resists a change in motion. There should be little disagreement about that. Standard introductory textbooks "define" it in this way for classical mechanics. Then when the authors introduce the special theory they do not give a new "definition" or mark in any way that they are starting to use the word to refer to a different property of a body. It is understood that they are using it in the same way, that is, with the same referent. [179] Changing the referent of a word is a sufficiently drastic procedure that one would indicate in some way that it was being done if one was doing it. No such indications are given. One can only conclude that the reference is not being changed.

The same can be said for many introductory relativity texts (e.g. Einstein, **Relativity**, pp. 44-45; A. Einstein, **The Meaning of Relativity**, 5th ed. (Princeton: Princeton University Press, 1955), pp. 46, 47; Pauli, **Relativity**, pp. 82, 83; Tolman, **Relativity**, pp. 42-45). I realize that many of the more recent 4-vector treatments do give a new referent to the word, but they also recognize that one does not have to proceed in that fashion, that most did not at an earlier time, and most do not yet (e.g. E.F. Taylor and J.A. Wheeler, **Spacetime Physics** (San Francisco: W.H. Freeman, 1966), pp. 105-109; R.B. Leighton, **Principles of Modern Physics** (New York: McGraw-Hill, 1959), pp. 35-56). If the 4-vector theorists have their way, the use of "mass" will shift, but it has not yet. And this is crucial here, for it the meaning variance theorists were right, it would be impossible for the referent not to have shifted in the transition from Newtonian physics.

If I may anticipate my conclusion, the reason for the proposed referential shift is simple; the earlier relativistic theorists who passed on our present use were more concerned with identifying the mass of which Newton spoke in the special theory in order to test the new theory and more generally to compare its claims with those of the earlier view. They found it, as I am in the process of arguing, in the relativistic mass. Now that the special theory has proved its superiority this concern is of secondary importance, and the 4-vector theorists have other major concerns, in particular, elegance and economy. And it is on these grounds that they want to change the referent. But even if they succeed, and I suspect they both will and ought to, the mass of which Newton spoke will still occur in the special theory as the relativistic mass. But this **is** by way of anticipation of my conclusion.

Since "mass" refers **at least** to that property in virtue of which a body resists a change in motion in the special theory, any differences in reference must be due to its referring to that property in virtue of which, etc., **and** something else, where the "something else" will distinguish the reference of "mass" in the special theory from that in classical theory. That is, it cannot be something like "...and which for elementary particles has a constant value in the reference frame which is at rest with respect to the observer", for that characteristic will not distinguish it from the referent in classical mechanics.

Kuhn claims that another characteristic is that it is not conserved. But this cannot be a necessary characteristic of the referent, for the statement that mass is not conserved would have to be self-referring, necessary, analytic and **a priori**, which it is not. It could be a

---

179 Again see: Feynman, **Lectures**, pp. 9-1, 15-1; Halliday and Resnick, **Physics**, pp. 68, 105; Shortley and Williams, **Principles**, pp. 52, 851-853. In one place Halliday and Resnick write: "Einstein's findings suggest that if physical laws were to be retained in the **classical** form the mass of a particle had to be redefined as $m = m_o /\sqrt{1-(v^2/c^2)}$." (**Ibid.**, p. 145, underline is mine). But in explaining the meaning of the equation they write: "...m is the mass of the particle" (**Ibid.**, p. 146), which shows that they are giving a new means of measuring mass, a new "quantitative definition" as they are sometimes called, but the reference of "m" has not been changed.

contingent characteristic if the special theory is true. But if it is true, then the referential stability theorist can say the same thing about "mass" in classical physics. That is, he can say that "mass" in Newtonian physics referred to a property of bodies which was not conserved, though this was not discovered until 1905. Thus there is no contrast to give us a difference of reference in both theories.

Again, other characteristics may be suggested, for example "which is a relation involving velocities between an object and a coordinate system". [180] This cannot be a necessary characteristic, for if it were, the statement that mass varies with velocity (or the quantitative statement) would be self-referring, etc. It could be a contingent characteristic (and I think it is), but in that case we can say that "mass" in Newtonian physics referred to a property which is a relation involving, etc. too, and so there is no contrast. Again, there are other characteristics which we may use to fix the reference, for example being that which the special theory **says** (claims) is conserved, being a relation involving velocities between an object and a coordinate system; but none of these will establish a difference in reference.

All of this shows that "mass" refers to that property of a body in virtue of which it resists a change of motion in **both** theories. And this is what I set out to show.

Three obstacles to unqualified acceptance of this conclusion exist: one is the independent arguments for meaning variance which have been dealt with in section 5.6; the other two are the arguments of the referential indeterminists (i.e. those who hold that reference is indeterminate in the important theoretical transitions).

Hartry Field, for example, has argued that the reference of "mass" in Newtonian mechanics is indeterminate:

> Before relativity theory was discovered (I will argue) the word "mass" was **referentially indeterminate**: it did not **lack** denotation, in any straightforward sense; on the contrary, there are **two** physical quantities that each satisfy the normal criteria for being the denotation of the term. [181]

He argues that there are two tenets of Newtonian theory which are central to Newtonian science, namely, (i) $p = mv$ (where p is the momentum, and v is the velocity), and (ii) for any two reference frames, mass with respect to frame 2 = mass with respect to frame 1. Relativity theory shows that the conjunction of (i) and (ii) is false but it does not show which conjunct is false. If (i) is true and (ii) is false, then "mass" in Newtonian physics denotes the relativistic mass. If (i) is false and (ii) is true, then it denotes the rest mass. But some physicists use the word "mass" in such a way that (i) is true and (ii) is false; others, such that (i) is false and (ii) is true; and the ratio is about 50-50. [182] There is nothing in Newtonian physcis or the special theory that would make us choose one alternative over the other and thus nothing that would make us think that "mass" in classical theory denoted relativistic rather than rest mass.

This argument will not do. First, the ratio of physicists who use the word "mass" in such a way that (i) is true and (ii) is false to those who do not is **not** 50-50. Of seventeen standard texts authored by such notables as Einstein, Pauli, Tolman, Rosser and Feynman, fifteen use "mass" in such a way that (i) is true and (ii) is false, that is, in the way that implies that "mass" is being used to denote the relativistic mass in both theories. [183] Only two used it the other way. Of those two, one's claim is false (Møller, as I shall show later) while the other (Goldstein) recognizes the accepted use, but suggests that it will not be with us for long. [184] Further, the standard description of the high velocity electron experiment is that it

180 Feyerabend, "Problems, Part I", p. 169.
181 Hartry Field, "Theory Change and the Indeterminacy of Reference", **The Journal of Philosophy** 70:14 (August 16, 1973) 466.
182 **Ibid.**, p. 469.
183 Pauli, **Relativity**, p. 83; Tolman, **Relativity**, pp. 44, 45; W.G.V. Rosser, **An Introduction to the Theory of Relativity** (London: Butterworths, 1964), pp. 179-180; Bohm, **The Special Theory of Relativity**, p. 81; A.S. Eddington, **The Mathematical Theory of Relativity** (Cambridge: Cambridge University Press, 1960), p. 30; Einstein, **Relativity**, p. 47; Rolf Nevanlinna, **Space, Time and Relativity** (Reading, Mass.: Addison-Wesley, 1968), p. 144; Arnold Sommerfield, **Electrodynamics** (New York: Academic, 1964), p. 263; R.P. Feynman, et. al., **Lectures** (Vol. 1), p. 16-6; Grant R. Fowles, **Analytical Mechanics** (New York: Rinehart & Winston, 1962), p. 266; Joos, **Theoretical Physics**, p. 254; John C. Slater and Nathaniel H. Frank, **Mechanics** (New York: McGraw-Hill, 1947), p. 5; A. d'Abro, **The Evolution of Scientific Thought**, 2nd ed. (New York: Dover, 1950), p. 157; S.J. Prokhovnik, **The Logic of Special Relativity** (Cambridge: Cambridge University Press, 1967), p. 10; Richard T. Weidner and Robert I. Sells, **Elementary Modern Physics** (Boston: Allyn & Bacon, 1960), pp. 64-68; A. Kyrala, **Theoretical Physics** (Philadelphia: W.B. Saunders, 1967), p. 255; Einstein, **Meaning of Relativity**, p. 47.
184 C. Møller, **The Theory of Relativity**, 2nd ed. (Oxford: Oxford University Press, 1972), pp. 66-68; and Goldstein, **Classical Mechanics**, pp. 204-250.

shows that in contrast to the assumption of classical theory, mass increases with velocity. [185] Obviously one is not talking about the rest mass here.

Second, Field's claim that there is nothing in Newtonian physics or the special theory that would make us choose the one alternative rather than the other is false. R.C. Tolman argued that only by supposing that "mass" in Newtonian theory refers to the relativistic mass can the conservation laws (linear momentum, in particular) hold in all coordinate systems; [186] and the conservation laws were and are well confirmed and of fundamental importance not only to the special theory but to classical mechanics. Tolman was apparently followed in this by most others. So there was something that **did** as a matter of historical fact make the physicists choose the one alternative rather than the other.

Finally, there is one consideration that **should** have made physicists believe that "mass" in Newtonian physics referred to the relativistic mass, namely, it could not have referred to the rest mass. I have argued that "mass" refers to that property of a body in virtue of which it resists a change in motion. But the rest mass is by definition that mass of a body which is **at rest** with respect to the observer's frame. It cannot, therefore, be the mass of a body which is moving with a **non-zero velocity** relative to the observer's frame and which resists a change in that motion (at best it is part of that). But **that** is what "mass" in classical mechanics refers to. Consequently, Field's conclusion is false.

Recently Arthur Fine has argued for the indeterminacy of reference on other grounds:

> The only evidence one can muster in support of a case for sameness or difference of reference is evidence as to classification output — what was (is) actually said to be what — and evidence as to patterns of argument, reasoning, or whatever that motivates the output....But in the cases of interest, the Kuhnian hypothesis, that the reference is determined by the conscientious classification behavior of average believers of the relevant theories...is cooked up precisely to mirror actual behavior patterns. Thus, the facts in these cases will always support a case for difference of reference. But, conversely, a good case for sameness of reference is likewise always available. For we can always...select whichever theory in the transition seems the best precursor to the scientific beliefs we now hold true....From this theoretical perspective, we can argue away discrepancies between our way with reference and actual classification behavior as plausible mistakes which holders of a flawed theory are bound to make. [187]

Thus

> ...in the situations of interest, whenever a case can be made for sameness of reference, an equally good case can be made for difference of reference, and conversely....I propose, then that we accept the cases that Kuhn and Feyerabend have called cases of "incommensurability" as genuine cases of indeterminacy with respect to sameness or difference of reference. [188]

This will not do. A good case for **p** looks like (though it need not be) a conclusive case for **p**. But difference in conscientious classification behavior does not look like a conclusive case for difference in reference. The conscientious behavior of most of the people of the western hemisphere at one time in the past would have placed the earth in the class of flat objects. [189] Present classification behavior would not. But this does not look like a conclusive case for difference of reference of either "earth" or "flat". It would, only if it looked like conclusive evidence that "earth" was used to refer to a flat object or "flat" was used to refer to surfaces like that of the earth. But it is absurd to suggest either of these. It follows that conscientious classification behavior does not always provide a good case for identity or difference of reference. And since there is no relevant difference between this case and the cases of interest, neither does conscientious classification behavior provide good evidence in those cases. By contrast the earlier arguments of this appendix show **at least** that a good case can be made for sameness of reference in one of the cases of interest. It follows that Fine's claim that an **equally good** case can be made for difference of reference as for sameness of reference is false.

185   Even the title of R.S. Farago and L. Janossy, "Review of the Experimental Evidence for the Law of Variation of Electron Mass with Velocity", **Il Nuovo Cimento**, 5 (1957) 1411, shows this.
186   Tolman, **Relativity**, pp. 43-45.
187   Arthur Fine, "How to Compare Theories: Reference and Change", **Noûs** 9 (1975) 27.
188   **Ibid.**
189   I realize I might be justly charged with presenting cases which are not genuine cases of classification behavior, but neither do Kuhn or Feyerabend (see their remarks on g [gravitational acceleration], "mass", "temperature", "entropy", "impetus", "space", and "energy" — none of which is a kind term as I understand that expression). And my aim is to get at their reasoning, not something which might be invented by Fine.

The converse is also false. "Caloric" in the theory of heat of Carnot and Clapeyron referred to caloric, a hypothetical material substance. "Molecular motion" in the kinetic theory of heat of, say, Boltzmann referred to molecular motion, which is not a material substance nor is it even supposed to be. It is categorically the wrong kind of thing to be a material substance. This is a better than good case for difference of reference. But not even a good case can be made for identity of reference. The only plausible candidate for the referent of both expressions is heat. But that caloric (if there were such a substance) would be a material substance is necessarily true, and that molecular motion is not a material substance is likewise necessarily true. If the two expressions referred to heat, caloric would have to be identical to molecular motion, the absurdity of which does not need to be explicated any further. So we cannot come near a good case, never mind a better than good case, for sameness of reference here. It follows that Fine's claim that an equally good case can be made for sameness of reference as for difference of reference is just false.

And with that **his** case for the indeterminacy of reference vanishes. The reference of "mass" in Newtonian mechanics **is** determinate; in particular it refers to the relativistic mass, or the same property as "mass" refers to in special relativity. We now have clear and free title to that claim.

It should be noted that one immediate consequence of this discussion is that the incommensurability thesis of Feyerabend and Kuhn is false. What is called the law of conservation of mass may be expressed "$\Sigma m_i = \text{constant}$" (read: the sum of the masses of the fundamental bodies is equal to a constant) in both classical mechanics and the special theory. All terms have the same referent ("m_i", "$=$", "constant") or the same meaning ("Σ") in both theories. So the affirmatives are identical. Consequently, the negation, "$\Sigma m_i \neq \text{constant}$", which is a consequence of special relativity **is** the denial of the classical law. It is clear, then, that we do have the law of conservation of mass in classical mechanics and **its** denial in special relativity. The two theories make contradictory claims and so the theories are commensurable, that is, are capable of being evaluated by a common standard.

BIBLIOGRAPHY

d'Abro, A. **The Evolution of Scientific Thought**. 2nd ed. New York: Dover, 1950.

Adler, Ronald; Bazin, Maurice; and Schiffner, Menahem. **Introduction to General Relativity**. New York: McGraw-Hill, 1965.

Ager, Tryg; Aronson, Jerrold L.; and Weingard, Robert. "Are Bridge Laws Really Necessary?" **Noûs** 8 (May, 1974) 119-134.

Alston, William P. **Philosophy of Language**. Englewood Cliffs: Prentice-Hall, 1964.

Anderson, James L. **Principles of Relativity Physics**. New York: Academic, 1967.

Andrews, C.L. **Optics of the Electromagnetic Spectrum**. Englewood Cliffs: Prentice-Hall, 1960.

Ayer, A.J. **Language, Truth and Logic**. 2nd ed. New York: Dover, 1952.

Bohm, David. "A Suggested Interpretation of the Quantum Theory in Terms of 'Hidden' Variables" I, II. **Physical Review** 85 (January, 1952) 166-179, 180-193.

_____. **Quantum Theory**. Englewood Cliffs: Prenice-Hall, 1951.

_____. **The Special Theory of Relativity**. New York: W.A. Benjamin, 1965.

Boltzmann, Ludwig. **Lectures on Gas Theory**. Trans. by Stephen G. Brush. Berkeley: University of California Press, 1964.

Boorse, Henry A. and Motz, Lloyd, eds. **The World of the Atom**. Vol. 2. New York: Basic Books, 1965.

Born, Max. **Einstein's Theory of Relativity.** Revised ed. New York: Dover, 1962.

_____; and Wolf, Emil. **Principles of Optics**. 3rd revised ed. Oxford: Pergamon Press, 1965.

Brittan, Gordon G., Jr. "Explanation and Reduction". **Journal of Philosophy** 67:13 (July 9, 1970) 446-457.

Brown, Lowell S. "Classical Limit and the WKB Approximation". **American Journal of Physics** 40 (March, 1972) 371-376.

Carnot, Sadi. **Reflections on the Motive Power of Fire**. Edited by E. Mendoza. New York: Dover, 1960.

Clagett, Marshall. **The Science of Mechanics in the Middle Ages**. Madison: University of Wisconsin Press, 1959.

Cohn, Jack. "Quantum Theory in the Classical Limit". **American Journal of Physics** 40 (March, 1972) 463-7.

Conant, James Bryant. "The Overthrow of the Phlogiston Theory: The Chemical Revolution of 1775-1789". **Harvard Case Histories in Experimental Science**. Vol. 1. Edited by James Bryant Conant and Leonard K. Nash. Cambridge: Harvard University Press, 1957.

Crawford, Franzo H. **Heat, Thermodynamics, and Statistical Physics**. New York: Harcourt, Brace & World, 1963.

Davis, Martin; and Hersch, Reuben. "Nonstandard Analysis". **Scientific American** 226:6 (June, 1972) 78-86.

Davydov, A.S. **Quantum Mechanics**. Reading, Mass.: Addison-Wesley, 1965.

Dirac, P.A.M. **The Principles of Quantum Mechanics**. 4th ed. Oxford: Clarendon Press, 1958.

Drude, Paul. **The Theory of Optics**. New York: Dover, 1959.

Dugas, René. **Mechanics in the Seventeenth Century**. New York: Central Book, 1958.

Duhem, Pierre. **The Aim and Structure of Physical Theory**. New York: Atheneum, 1962.

Eddington, A.S. **The Mathematical Theory of Relativity.** Cambridge: Cambridge University Press, 1960.

Einstein, Albert. "The Foundation of the General Theory of Relativity". **The Principle of Relativity**. New York: Dover, 1928, pp. 109-164.

. **The Meaning of Relativity**. 5th ed. Princeton: Princeton University Press, 1955.

. **Investigations on the Theory of the Brownian Movement**. New York: Dover, 1956.

. **Relativity: The Special and the General Theory**. 15th ed., enlarged. London: Methuen, 1959.

Farago, P.S. and Janossy, L. "Review of the Experimental Evidence for the Law of Variation of Electron Mass with Velocity". **Il Nuovo Cimento** 5 (1957) 1411-36.

Fermi, Enrico. **Thermodynamics**. New York: Dover, 1936.

Feyerabend, P.K. "Explanation, Reduction, and Empiricism". **Minnesota Studies in the Philosophy of Science**. Vol. 3. Edited by Herbert Feigl and Grover Maxwell. Minneapolis: University of Minnesota Press, 1962, pp. 28-97.

. "How to Be a Good Empiricist: A Plea for Tolerance in Matters Epistemological". **Philosophy of Science: The Delaware Seminar**. Edited by Bernard Baumrin. New York: Interscience, 1963, pp. 3-39.

. "On the 'Meaning' of Scientific Terms". **Theories and Observation in Science**. Edited by Richard E. Grandy. Englewood Cliffs: Prentice-Hall, 1973, pp. 176-183. Originally in: **Journal of Philosophy** 12 (May 13, 1965) 333-377.

. "Problems of Empiricism". **Beyond the Edge of Certainty**. Edited by R. Colodny. Englewood Cliffs: Prentice-Hall, 1965, pp. 145-260.

. "Reply to Criticism". **Boston Studies in the Philosophy of Science**. Vol. 2. Edited by Robert S. Cohen and Marx W. Wartofsky. New York: Humanities, 1965, pp. 223-261.

. "On a Recent Critique of Complementarity, Part I". **Philosophy of Science** 35:4 (December, 1968) 309-331.

. "Against Method: Outline of an Anarchistic Theory of Knowledge". **Analyses of Theories and Methods of Physics and Psychology**. Vol. 4 in **Minnesota Studies in the Philosophy of Science**. Edited by Michael Radner and Stephen Winokur. Minneapolis: University of Minnesota Press, 1970, pp. 17-130.

. "Problems of Empiricism, Part II". **The Nature and Function of Scientific Theories**. Edited by Robert G. Colodny. Pittsburgh: University of Pittsburgh Press, 1970, pp. 275-353.

Feynman, Richard P.; Leighton, Robert B.; and Sands, Matthew. **The Feynman Lectures on Physics**. Vol. 1. Reading, Mass.: Addison-Wesley, 1963.

Field, Hartry. "Theory Change and the Indeterminacy of Reference". **The Journal of Philosophy** 70:14 (August 16, 1973) 462-81.

Fine, Arthur. "How to Compare Theories: Reference and Change". **Noûs** 9 (1975) 17-32.

Fong, Peter. **Foundations of Thermodynamics**. New York: Oxford University Press, 1963.

Ford, Kenneth W. **The World of Elementary Particles**. New York: Blaisdell, 1963.

Fowler, R.H. **Statistical Mechanics**. Cambridge: Cambridge University Press, 1966.

Fowles, Grant R. **Analytical Mechanics**. New York: Rinehart & Winston, 1962.

Frege, Gottlieb. "On the Foundations of Geometry". Translated by M.E. Szabo. **Philosophical Review** 69 (1960) 3-16.

Gibbs, J. Willard. **Elementary Principles in Statistical Mechanics**. New York: Dover, 1962.

Glymour, Clark. "On Some Patterns of Reduction". **Philosophy of Science** 37 (Sept., 1970) 340-353.

Goldstein, Herbert. **Classical Mechanics.** Reading, Mass.: Addison-Wesley, 1959.

Halliday, David and Resnick, Robert. **Physics for Students of Science and Engineering**. Combined ed. New York: John Wiley & Sons, 1960, 1962.

Hanson, Norwood Russell. **Patterns of Discovery**. Cambridge: Cambridge University Press, 1961.

Heisenberg, Werner. **The Physical Principles of the Quantum Theory**. New York: Dover, 1930.

Hempel, Carl G. "Deductive-Nomological vs. Statistical Explanation". **Minnesota Studies in the Philosophy of Science**. Vol. 3. Edited by Herbert Feigl and Grover Maxwell. Minneapolis: University of Minnesota Press, 1962, pp. 98-169.

. "Reduction: Ontological and Linguistic Facets". **Philosophy, Science and Method**. Edited by S. Morgenbesser, P. Suppes, and M. White. New York: St. Martin's Press, 1969, pp. 179-199.

Hesse, Mary B. "Review of Israel Scheffler's **Science and Subjectivity**". **The British Journal for the Philosophy of Science** 19 (1968) 177.

The Structure of Scientific Inference. London: MacMillan, 1974, chapters I and II.

Hofstadter, R. "Structure of Nuclei and Nucleons". **Science** 136 (1962) 1013-1022.

Hooker, C.A. "Non-Conventionalist Classical Mechanics". **Boston Studies in the Philosophy of Science**. Vol. 13. **Logical and Epistemological Studies in Contemporary Physics**. Edited by Robert S. Cohen and Marx W. Wartofsky. Dordrecht: D. Reidel, 1974.

Jammer, Max. **Concepts of Force**. New York: Harper & Brothers, 1957.

. **Concepts of Space**. New York: Harper & Brothers, 1960.

. **Concepts of Mass**. New York: Harper & Row, 1961.

. **The Conceptual Development of Quantum Mechanics**. New York: McGraw-Hill, 1966.

Joos, Georg. **Theoretical Physics**. 3rd ed. New York: Hafner, 1958.

Kaplan, Irving. **Nuclear Physics**. Reading, Mass.: Addison-Wesley, 1963.

Kemble, Edwin C. **The Fundamental Principles of Quantum Mechanics**. New York: Dover, 1958.

Kepler, Johann. **The Laws of Planetary Motion**. Selection included in **The Origins and Growth of Physical Sciences**. Vol. 1. Edited by D.L. Hurd and J.J. Kipling. Harmondsworth: Penguin Books, 1964, p. 132.

Khinchin. A.E. **Mathematical Foundations of Statistical Mechanics**. New York: Dover, 1949.

Kline, Morris. **Mathematical Thought from Ancient to Modern Times**. New York: Oxford University Press, 1972.

Kobe, Donald H. "Comments on the Classical Limit of Quantum Mechanics". **American Journal of Physics** 42:1 (January, 1974) 73-74.

Kopp, Herman F.M. **Geschichte der Chemie**. Brunswick: 1843, pp. 150f. Cited in J.R. Partington and Douglas McKie, "Historical Studies on the Phlogiston Theory—I. The Levity of Phlogiston". **Annals of Science** 2 (October 15, 1937) 361-404.

Kordig, Carl R. **Justification of Scientific Change**. Dordrecht: D. Reidel,–1971.

Kottler, F. "Diffraction at a Black Screen; Part I: Kirchoff's Theory". **Progress in Optics**. Vol. 4. Edited by E. Wolf. Amsterdam: North-Holland, 1965, pp. 283-314.

. "Diffraction at a Black Screen; Part II: Electromagnetic Theory". **Progress in Optics**. Vol. 6. Edited by E. Wolf. Amsterdam: North-Holland, 1967, pp. 333-377.

Kripke, Saul. "Identity and Necessity". **Identity and Individuation**. Edited by Milton K. Munitz. New York: New York University Press, 1971, pp. 135-164.

. "Naming and Necessity". **Semantics of Natural Language**. Edited by Gilbert Harmon and Donald Davidson. Dordrecht: D. Reidel, 1972, pp. 253-355; 763-769.

Kuasnica, J. **Physical Fields**. London: Iliffe Books, 1964, p. 177.

Kuhn, Thomas S. **The Structure of Scientific Revolutions**. 2nd ed., enlarged. Chicago: The University of Chicago Press, 1970.

Kyrala, A. **Theoretical Physics**. Philadelphia: W.B. Saunders, 1967.

Lanczos, Cornelius. **Space Through the Ages**. New York: Academic, 1970.

Landau, L.D., and Lifshitz, E.M. **Quantum Mechanics: Non-Relativistic Theory.** 2nd ed. Revised and enlarged. Oxford: Pergamon Press, 1965.

Leighton, Robert B. **Principles of Modern Physics.** New York: McGraw-Hill, 1959.

Lemmon, E.J. "Sentences, Statements and Propositions". **British Analytical Philosophy**. Edited by Bernard Williams and Alan Montefiore. London: Routledge & Kegan Paul, 1966, pp. 87-107.

Lightstone, A.H. "Infinitesimals". **The American Mathematical Monthly** 79:3 (March, 1972) 242-251.

Loeb, Leonard B. **The Kinetic Theory of Gases**. 3rd ed. New York: Dover, 1961.

Lorentz, H.A.; Einstein, A.; Minkowski, H.; and Weyl, H. **The Principles of Relativity**. New York: Dover, 1923.

Luneberg, R.K. **Mathematical Theory of Optics**. Berkeley: University of California Press, 1966.

Mates, Benson. **Elementary Logic**. 2nd ed. New York: Oxford University Press, 1972.

Maxwell, James Clerk. **A Treatise on Electricity and Magnetism**. Vol. 2. New York: Dover, 1952.

Mellor, J.W. **Higher Mathematics for Students of Chemistry and Physics**. New York: Dover, 1955.

Mendoza, E. "A Sketch for a History of Early Thermodynamics". **Physics Today** 14 (February, 1961) 32-42.

. "A Sketch for a History of the Kinetic Theory of Gases". **Physics Today** 14 (March, 1961) 36-39.

Merzbacher, Eugen. **Quantum Mechanics**. New York: John Wiley & Sons, 1961.

Messiah, Albert. **Quantum Mechanics**. Vols. 1 & 2. Amsterdam: North-Holland, 1961, 1962.

Minkowski, H. "Space and Time". **The Principle of Relativity**. New York: Dover, 1923, pp. 73-91.

Misner, Charles W.; Thorne, Kip S.; and Wheeler, John Archibald. **Gravitation.** San Francisco: W.H. Freeman, 1973.

Møller, C. **The Theory of Relativity.** 2nd ed. Oxford: Oxford University Press, 1972.

Nagel, Ernest. **The Structure of Science.** New York: Harcourt, Brace & World, 1961, pp. 336-397.

―――. "Issues in the Logic of Reductive Explanations". **Mind, Science and History.** Vol. 2. Edited by Howard E. Kiefer and Milton K. Munitz. Albany: State University of New York Press, 1970, pp. 117-137.

Nevanlinna, Rolf. **Space, Time and Relativity.** Reading, Mass.: Addison-Wesley, 1968.

Newton, Isaac. **Mathematical Principles.** Vol. 1. Translated by Andrew Motte. Revised by Florian Cajori. Berkeley: University of California Press, 1962.

Nickles, Thomas. "Two Concepts of Intertheoretic Reduction". **The Journal of Philosophy** 70:7 (April 12, 1973) 181-201.

Page, Edgar. "Reference and Propositional Identity". **Philosophical Review** 79 (January, 1970) 43-62.

Page, Leigh. **Introduction to Theoretical Physics.** 3rd ed. Princeton: D. Van Nostrand, 1952.

Partington, J.R. **A Short History of Chemistry.** New York: Harper & Brothers, 1960.

Pauli, W. **Theory of Relativity.** Oxford: Pergamon Press, 1958.

Prokhovnik, S.J. **The Logic of Special Relativity.** Cambridge: Cambridge University Press, 1967.

Putnam, H. "How Not to Talk About Meaning". **Boston Studies in the Philosophy of Science.** Vol. 2. Edited by Robert S. Cohen and Marx W. Wartofsky. New York: Humanities, 1965, pp. 205-222.

Reif, F. "Superfluidity and 'Quasi-Particles'". **Scientific American** 203 (Nov., 1960) 138-150.

Riemann, Bernard. "On the Hypotheses which Lie at the Foundations of Geometry". **A Source-Book in Mathematics.** Vol. 2. Edited by David Eugene Smith. New York: Dover, 1959, pp. 411-425.

Robinson, Abraham. **Non-Standard Analysis.** Amsterdam: North-Holland, 1966.

―――. "Metamathematical Problems". **The Journal of Symbolic Logic** 38:3 (Sept., 1973) 500-516.

―――. "Standard and Nonstandard Number Systems". **Nieuw Archief voor Wiskunde** 21:3 (1973) 115-133.

Roll-Hansen, Nils. "On the Reduction of Biology to Physical Science". **Synthese** 20 (1969) 277-289.

Rosen, Nathan. "The Relation Between Classical and Quantum Mechanics". **American Journal of Physics** 32 (1964) 597-600.

Rosser, W.G.V. **An Introduction to the Theory of Relativity.** London: Butterworths, 1964.

Rothman, Milton. **Discovering the Natural Laws.** Garden City: Doubleday, 1972.

Ruddick, William. "Physical Equations and Identity". **Identity and Individuation.** Edited by Milton K. Munitz. New York: New York University Press, 1971.

Ruelle, David. **Statisical Mechanics: Rigorous Results.** New York: W.A. Benjamin, 1969.

Sakurai, J.J. **Advanced Quantum Mechanics.** Reading, Mass.: Addison-Wesley, 1967.

Schaffner, Kenneth F. "Approaches to Reduction". **Philosophy of Science** 34:2 (June, 1967) 137-147.

Scheffler, Israel. **Science and Subjectivity.** Indianapolis: Bobbs-Merrill, 1967.

Schiff, Leonard I. **Quantum Mechanics**. 2nd ed. New York: McGraw-Hill, 1955.

Schild, A. "Gravitational Theories of the Whitehead Type and the Principle of Equivalence". **Evidence for Gravitational Theories**. Edited by C. Møller. New York: Academic, 1962.

. "Lectures on General Relativity Theory". **Relativity and Cosmology**. Edited by Jürgen Ehlers. Providence: American Mathematical Society, 1967.

Schwinger, Julian. **Particles, Sources, and Fields.** Reading, Mass.: Addison-Wesley, 1970.

Shortley, George and Williams, Dudley. **Principles of College Physics**. Englewood Cliffs: Prentice-Hall, 1959.

Sklar, Lawrence. "Types of Inter-Theoretic Reduction". **British Journal for the Philosophy of Science** 18 (1967) 109-124.

. "The Evolution of the Problem of the Unity of Science". **Philosophical Foundations of Science**. Edited by R.J. Seeger and R.S. Cohen. Dordrecht: D. Reidel, 1974, pp. 535-545.

Slater, John C. and Frank, Nathaniel H. **Mechanics**. New York: McGraw-Hill, 1947.

Smart, J.J.C. "Conflicting Views About Explanation". **Boston Studies in the Philosophy of Science**. Vol. 2. Edited by Robert S. Cohen and Marx W. Wartofsky. New York: Humanities, 1965, pp. 157-169.

. **Between Science and Philosophy**. New York: Random House, 1968.

Sommerfeld, Arnold. **Lectures on Theoretical Physics**. Vol. 4. **Optics**. New York: Academic, 1954.

Lectures on Theoretical Physics. Vol. 3: **Electrodynamics**. New York: Academic, 1964.
Lectures on Theoretical Physics. Vol. 5: **Thermodynamics and Statistical Mechanics**. New York: Academic, 1964.

Synge, J.L. **Relativity: The Special Theory**. 2nd ed. Amsterdam: North-Holland, 1965.

Taylor, Edwin F. and Wheeler, John Archibald. **Spacetime Physics**. San Francisco: W.H. Freeman, 1966.

Tolman, Richard C. **Relativity, Thermodynamics, and Cosmology**. Oxford: Clarendon Press, 1934.

. **The Principles of Statistical Mechanics**. Oxford: Oxford University Press, 1938.

Wannier, Gregory H. "Quantum-Mechanical Proof of the Second Law". **American Journal of Physics** 33:3 (March, 1965) 222-225.

. **Statistical Physics**. New York: John Wiley & Sons, 1966.

Webster, Arthur Gordon. **The Dynamics of a Particle**. 2nd ed. New York: Dover, 1912.

Weidner, Richard T. and Sells, Robert I. **Elementary Modern Physics**. Boston: Allyn & Bacon, 1960.

Wheeler, Lynde Phelps. **Josiah Willard Gibbs: The History of a Great Mind.** New Haven: Yale University Press, 1962.

Whittaker, Sir Edmund. **A History of the Theories of Aether and Electricity**. Vol. 2: **The Modern Theories 1900-1926**. New York: Harper & Brothers, 1960.

Wittgenstein, Ludwig. **Philosophische Bemerkungen**. Oxford: Basil Blackwell, 1964.

Wöhler, Fredrich. "On the Artificial Production of Urea". **Source Book in Chemistry: 1400-1900**. Edited by Henry M. Leicester and Herbert S. Klickstein. Cambridge, Mass.: Harvard University Press, 1952.

Yoshida, Ronald M. "Von Neumann's Proof and Hidden Variables". Ph.D. dissertation, University of Washington, 1971, pp. 194-203.